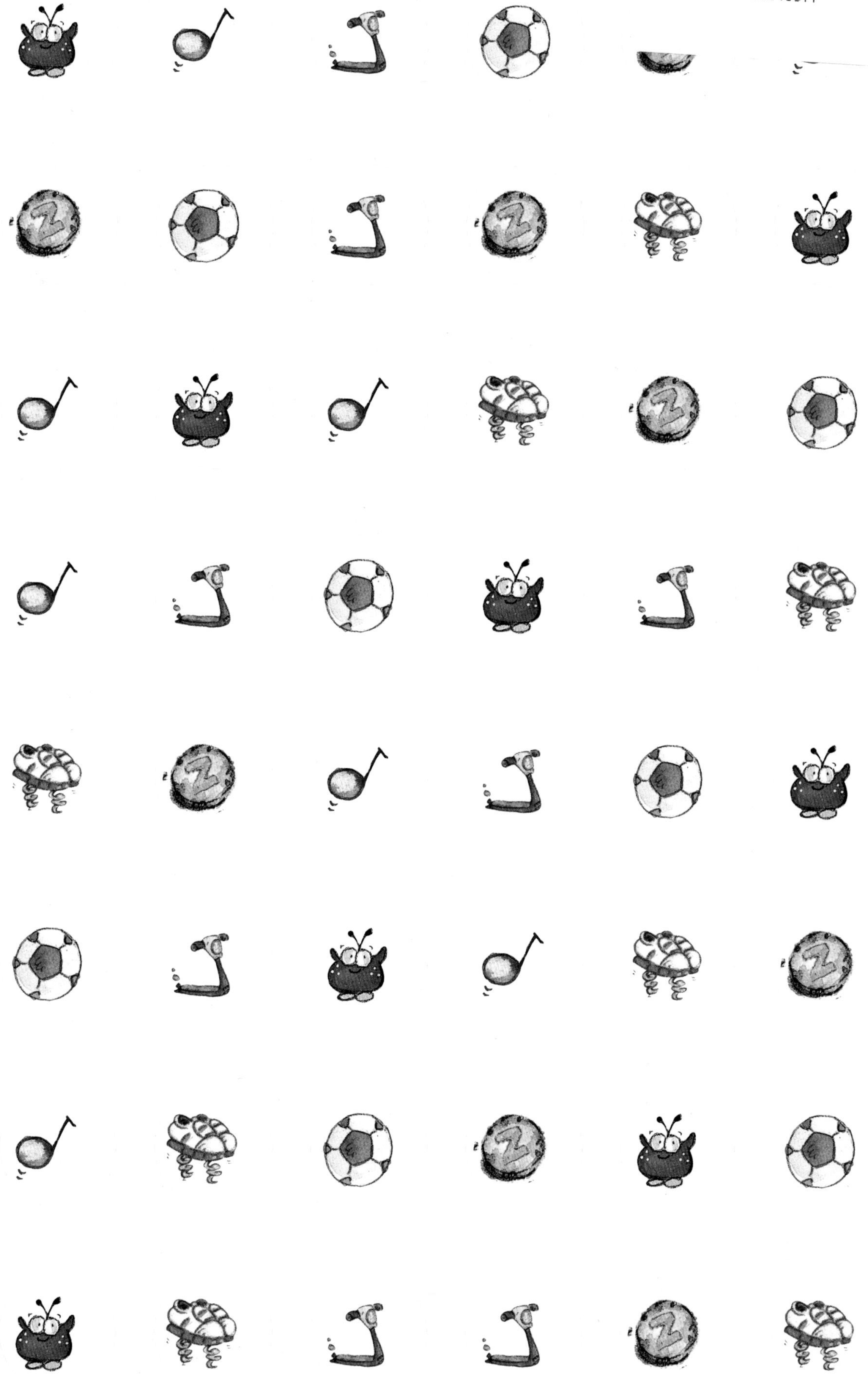

Letts

You think *you* have a long journey to school? Meet the Alien Club, a group of jolly aliens from the planet Dunk. They all entered a competition and won first prize – to go to school on planet Earth, six thousand light years away! Lucky their space-mobile runs on recycled rubbish and can travel a hundred light years in a heartbeat!

Meet **Nok**, who finds football much easier than school, but tries all the same!

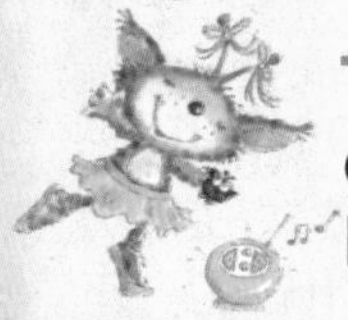

Twinx, who loves ribbons, dancing and her toy friend Mini T.

Bouncing **Pogo**, who just can't stand still!

Pogo's pet dog, the rather less lively **Zen**, who won't get out of bed for less than a Z cookie or two.

Zara P, zip zip zipping around on her scooter and making notes on everything she sees.

And **Zing**, who loves his music most of all, but thinks school is pretty cool too!

Now the Alien Club want to pass on everything they have learnt to you. All you have to do is work your way through these tests and not only will you be the cleverest Earthling around, you'll become a member of the Alien Club too! Out of this world!!!

THE ALIEN CLUB

Maths 8–9

Paul Broadbent

TEST 1

Number sequences

Hello there, I'm Zen! My lively pal Pogo wants me to count his bounces… in 5s! That wouldn't be so bad, but he wants me to start from 3.
It's OK though, because I can see a pattern.
3 8 13 18 23 28…
Sequences are fun! You just need to look at the difference between each number to spot the pattern. Relax – you can do this!

Fill in the missing numbers for each sequence.

1	47	43	39		31		
2	29	38		56			83
3		101	111		131	141	
4	1	8	15				43
5	87	82			67	62	
6	113	111		107		103	
7	1	10	19	28			
8	215	205			175		155
9	62	58			46	42	
10				105	100	95	90
11	65	68	71	74			
12	97	94			85	82	

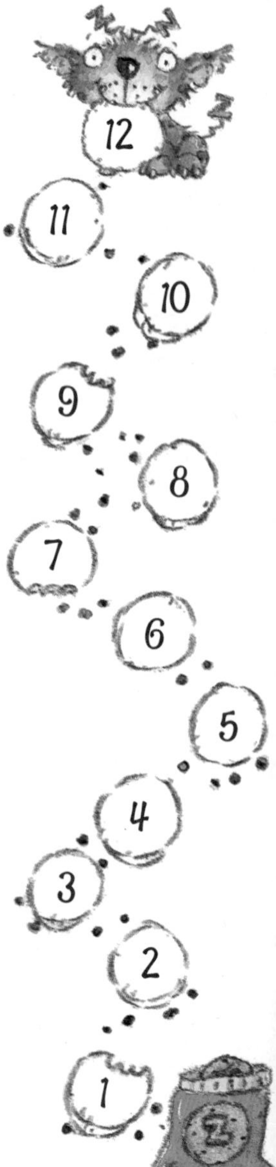

Good work! Have a Z cookie sticker for your certificate at the back of the book.

Colour in your score.

Addition and subtraction facts

Boing, boing, boing! I'm Pogo and I'm always just a bounce away! Zeros are great. You can make whole numbers 10 times bigger with an extra zero and 100 times bigger with two zeros. Look at the pattern:

$3 \times 1 = 3$ $8 \times 1 = 8$

$3 \times 10 = 30$ $8 \times 10 = 80$

$3 \times 100 = 300$ $8 \times 100 = 800$

This makes adding and subtracting these bigger numbers really easy.

$3 + 8 = 11$ $30 + 80 = 110$ $300 + 800 = 1100$

Ready, steady, bounce!

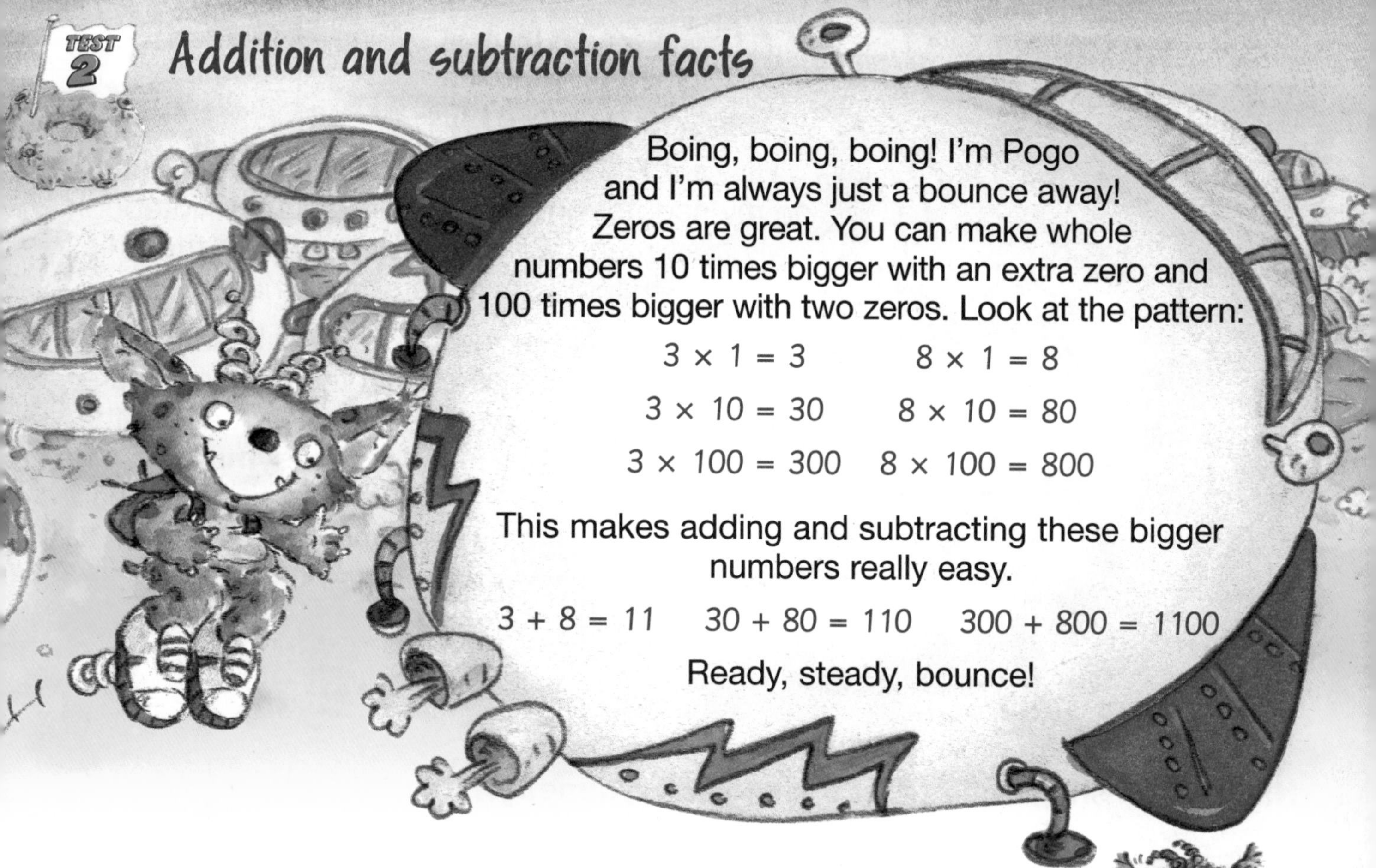

Fill in the missing numbers. Time yourself to test your speed.

1 $40 + \boxed{} = 100$

2 $900 + 500 = \boxed{}$

3 $\boxed{} + 600 = 1100$

4 $70 + 90 = \boxed{}$

5 $80 + \boxed{} = 160$

6 $\boxed{} + 400 = 1300$

7 $140 - 80 = \boxed{}$

8 $120 - \boxed{} = 70$

9 $\boxed{} - 600 = 900$

10 $170 - 120 = \boxed{}$

11 $\boxed{} - 80 = 30$

12 $1900 - \boxed{} = 1300$

Put a spring in your step! Have a springy sticker for your certificate at the back of the book.

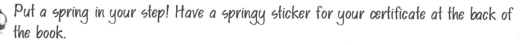

Colour in your score.

TEST 3

Shapes and symmetry

Hi! Zara P, that's me and I like zipping around on my scooter and making notes in my notebook! My friend Zing wants me to show him that this triangle shape is symmetrical.

Never fear, ZP is here! I can just fold it in half so that the two halves are the same. If I open it out again, the fold line is the **line of symmetry**. One half is the reflection of the other half, so it's a symmetrical shape.

Name each shape and draw the lines of symmetry.

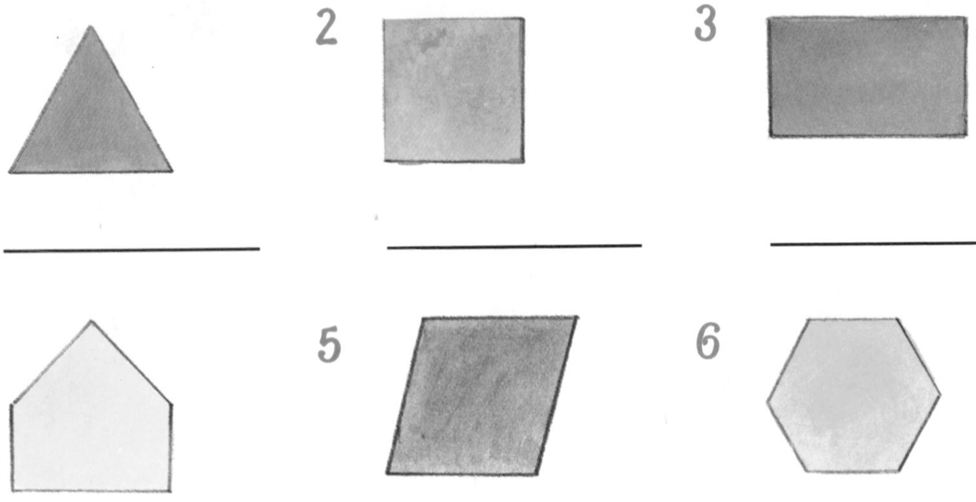

1 ______________

2 ______________

3 ______________

4 ______________

5 ______________

6 ______________

The dotted lines are the lines of symmetry for each shape. Draw the reflection of each shape.

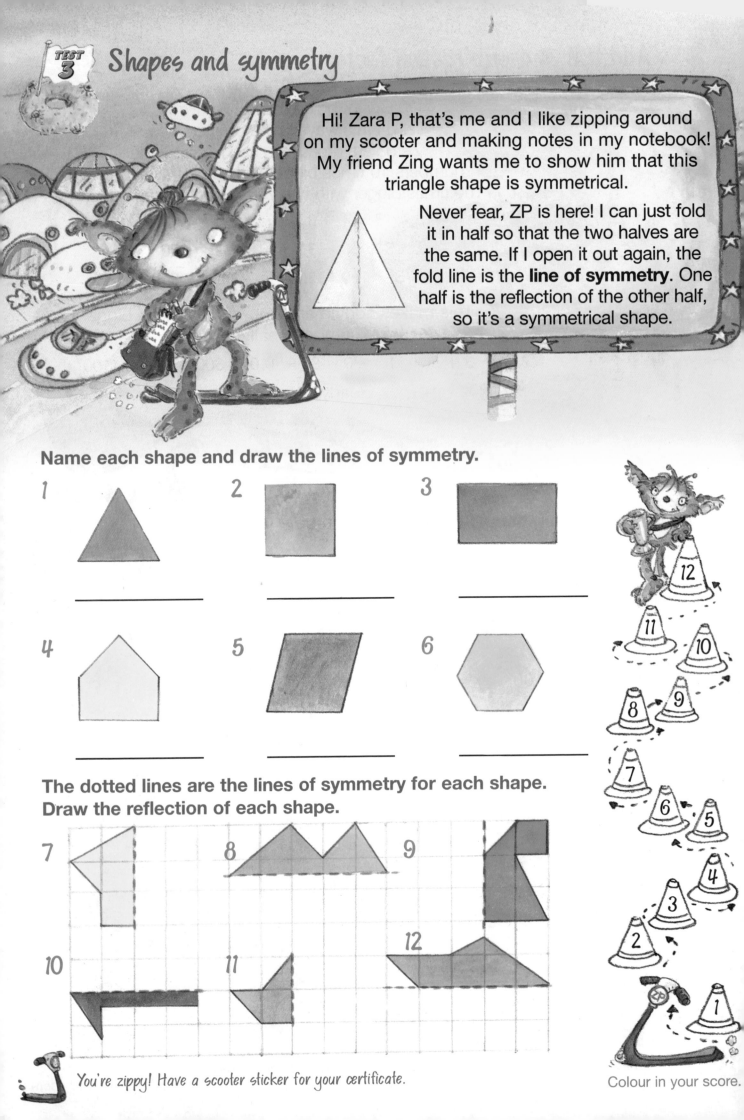

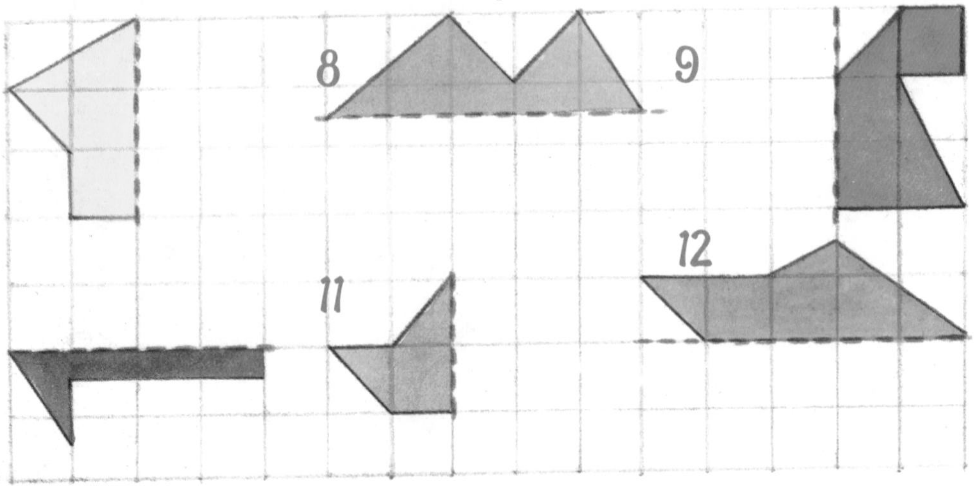

Colour in your score.

You're zippy! Have a scooter sticker for your certificate.

TEST 4 4-digit numbers

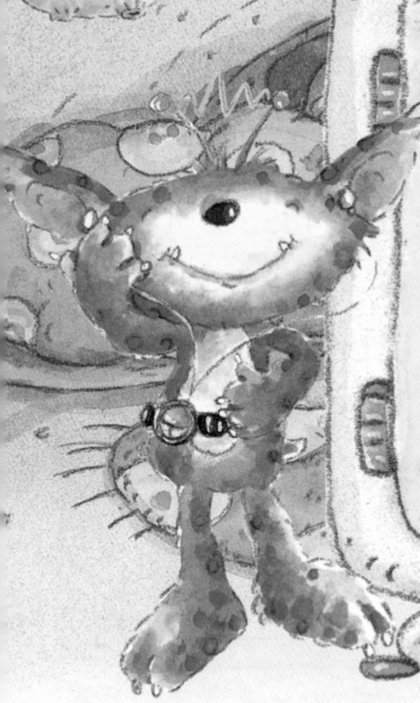

Hey there! My name's Zing – music's my thing. Numbers are fun too, though! There are so many things you can do with them. The digits 4, 3, 8 and 5, for instance, can make lots of different numbers, just by changing the order. Look at this:

Th	H	T	U	
4	3	8	5	4000 + 300 + 80 + 5 = 4385
8	4	5	3	8000 + 400 + 50 + 3 = 8453
5	8	3	4	5000 + 800 + 30 + 4 = 5834

See? Wow!

Fill in the missing numbers for each of these.

1	6712 =		+	700	+	10	+	
2	8993 =	8000	+		+	90	+	
3	4156 =		+	100	+		+	6
4	2356 =	2000	+		+	50	+	
5	7598 =		+	500	+		+	
6	2115 =	2000	+		+		+	
7	3965 =		+		+	60	+	
8	1254 =	1000	+		+		+	
9	3489 =		+		+		+	
10	6932 =		+		+		+	
11	4375 =		+		+		+	
12	7997 =		+		+		+	

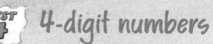

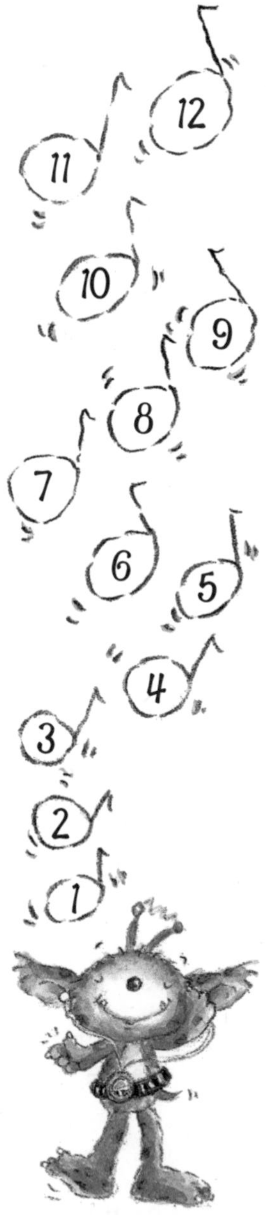

Easy! Have a musical sticker for your certificate.

Colour in your score.

Comparing and ordering numbers

Hi, I'm Nok. I'm football crazy! I scored 4855 points on a computer footy game, but I can't work out if it beats my best score of 4585 points. I'd better look at each digit:

4000 + 800 + 50 + 5 = 4855

4000 + 500 + 80 + 5 = 4585

The thousands are the same, but 800 is more than 500, so I've just beaten my best score! Goal!

Remember:

< means 'is less than'   4585 < 4855

> means 'is greater than' 4855 > 4585

Write the correct sign < or > in each football.

1 3056 2994

2 7445 7552

3 4921 4918

4 6003 5999

5 2192 2095

6 7222 7219

7 4187 4184

8 6933 6951

9 9022 9104

10 5252 2525

11 9685 9856

12 2800 2099

 Goal! Have a football sticker.

Colour in your score.

Test 6 Mental addition and subtraction

Hello, I'm Twinx and this is my toy friend Mini T. We like this puzzle. The bottom two numbers add up to the top one, 18 + 12 = 30.

	30	
18		12

Now, how can I work out these other two?

	☐	
25		35

25 + 35 = ☐ Add the tens and the ones. The missing number must be 60.

	46	
☐		24

I can swap these around, so it's – ☐ + 24 = 46

46 – 24 = ☐ The missing number is 22. Hurray!

Fill in the missing numbers.

No.	Top	Bottom left	Bottom right
1	☐	32	29
2	☐	46	18
3	67	☐	41
4	63	28	☐
5	☐	37	56
6	82	☐	49
7	71	36	☐
8	94	☐	65
9	☐	48	47
10	91	62	☐
11	84	☐	59
12	☐	54	47

Colour in your score.

Hurray! Have a Mini T sticker.

Area and perimeter

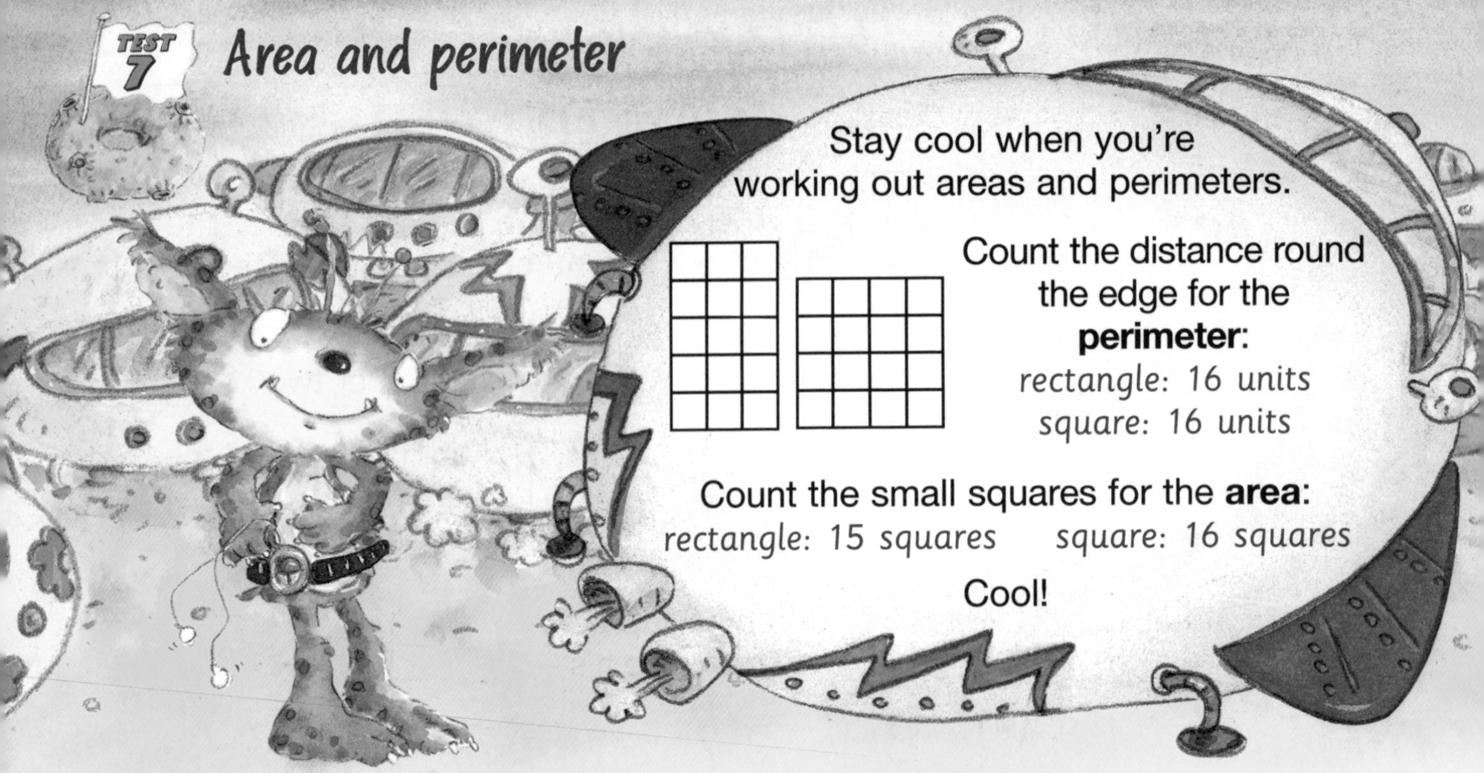
TEST 7
Stay cool when you're working out areas and perimeters.
Count the distance round the edge for the **perimeter**:
rectangle: 16 units
square: 16 units
Count the small squares for the **area**:
rectangle: 15 squares
square: 16 squares
Cool!

Find the area and perimeter of each shape.

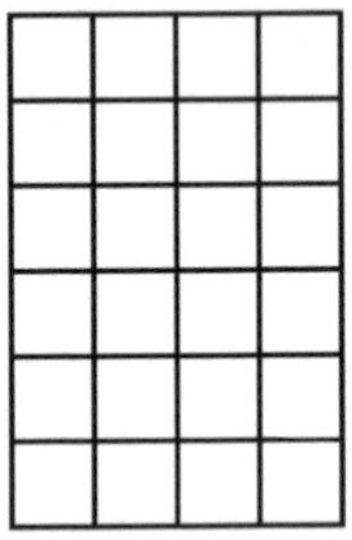

1 area = ________ squares

2 perimeter = ________ units

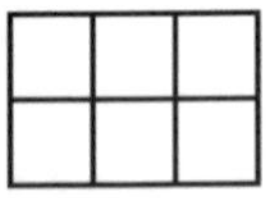

3 area = ________ squares

4 perimeter = ________ units

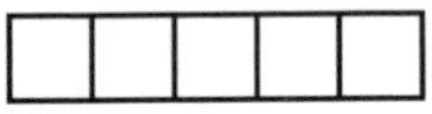

5 area = ________ squares

6 perimeter = ________ units

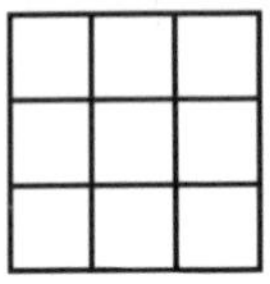

7 area = ________ squares

8 perimeter = ________ units

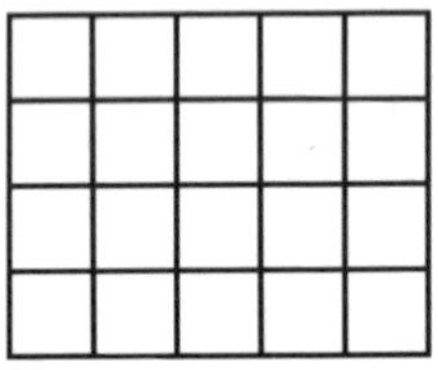

9 area = ________ squares

10 perimeter = ________ units

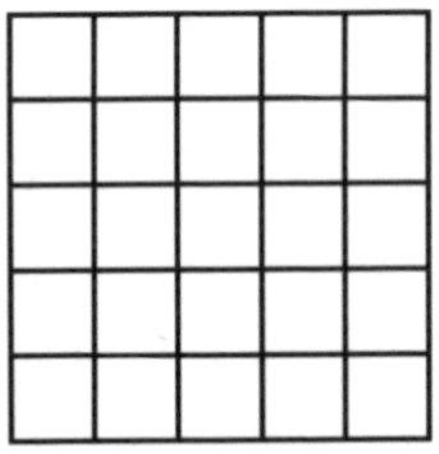

11 area = ________ squares

12 perimeter = ________ units

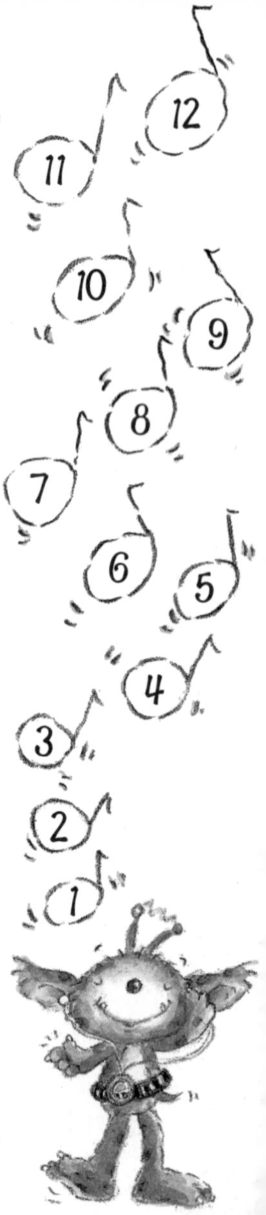

Easy! Have a musical sticker.

Colour in your score.

Decimal numbers

Boing, boing, boing! Decimal points are small, but they're very important. They separate whole numbers from fractions. The first digit after the decimal point shows tenths:

$$8.6 = 8 + \frac{6}{10}$$

ones   tenths

8.6

8 |————————————————| 9

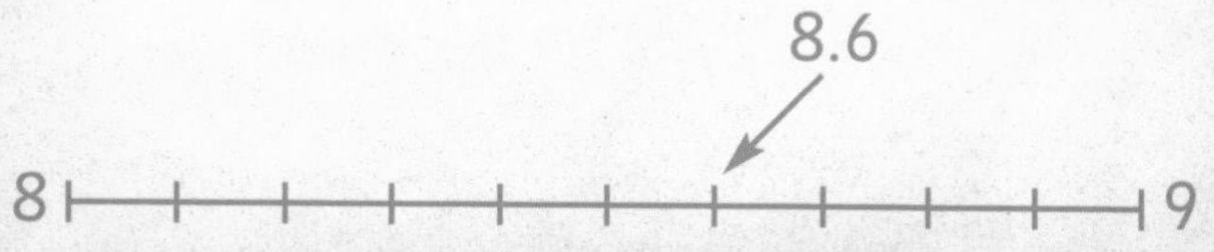

Write the decimals on the number lines.

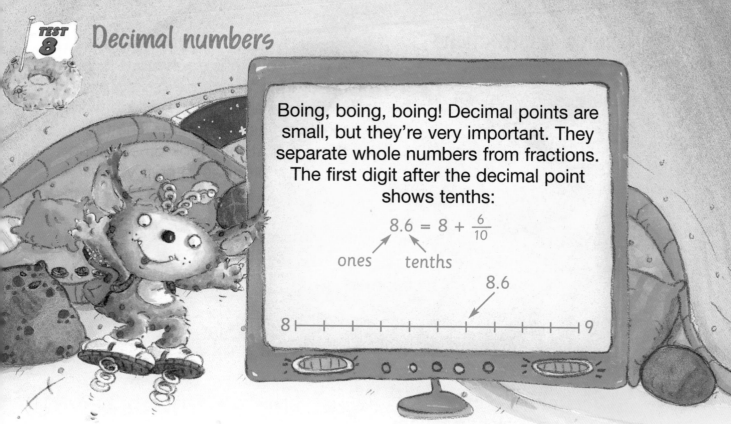

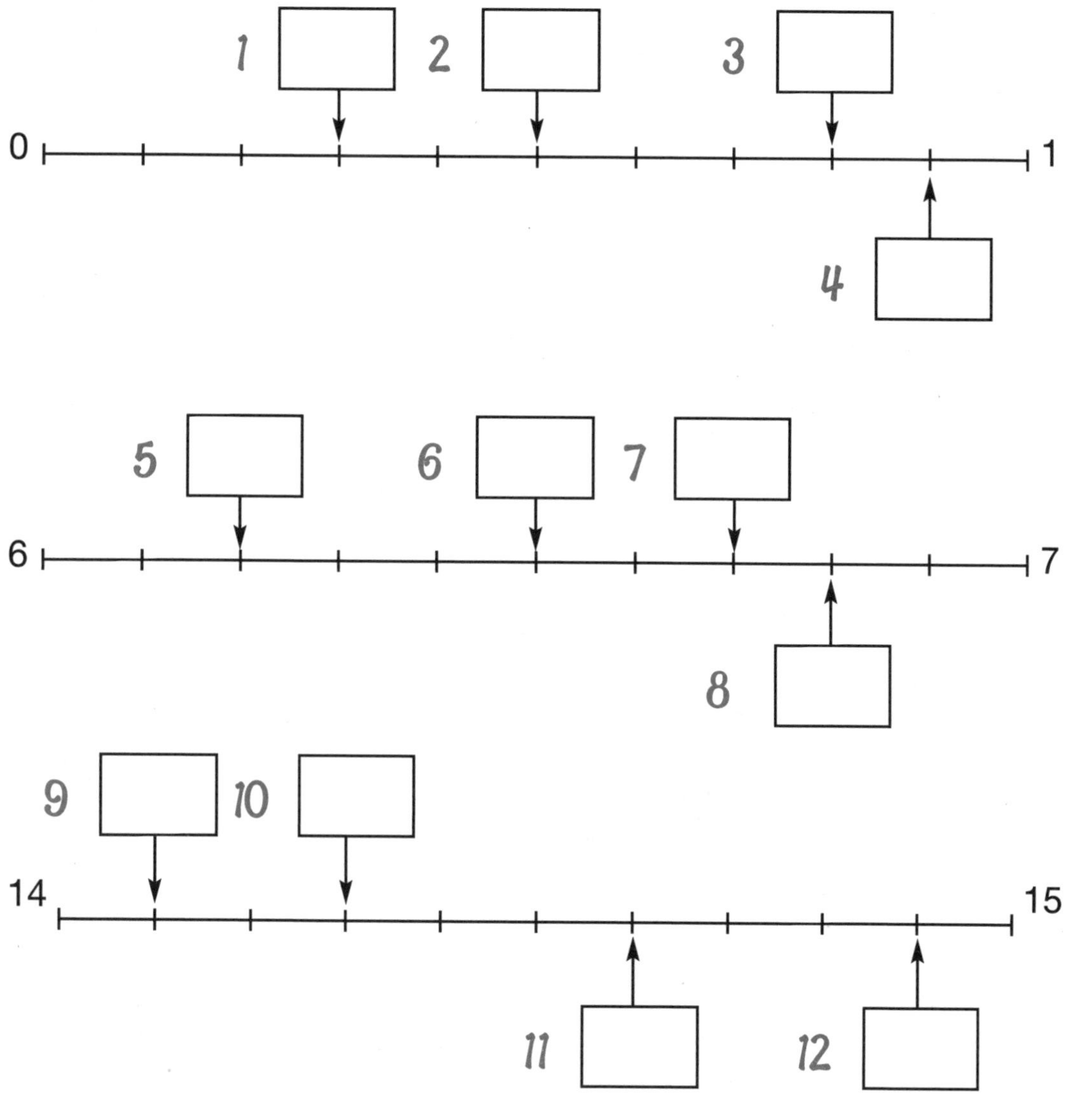

Colour in your score.

Equivalent fractions

Zip, zip, zip!
Did you know that **equivalent** is just a big word for 'the same', so equivalent fractions are fractions that are worth the same as each other. The tricky thing is that they look different, so draw pictures to help you.

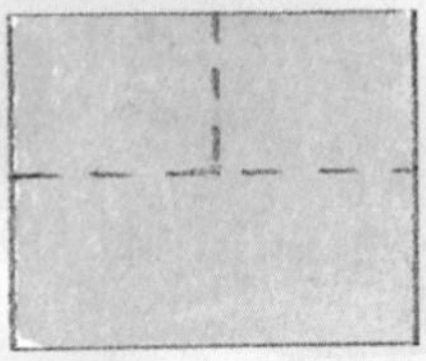

$$\frac{1}{2} = \frac{2}{4}$$

Complete these equivalent fractions.

1 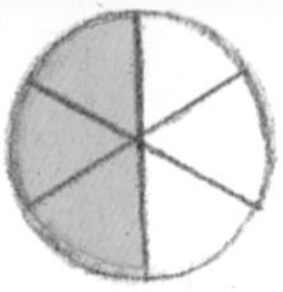 $\frac{\square}{6} = \frac{\square}{2}$

2 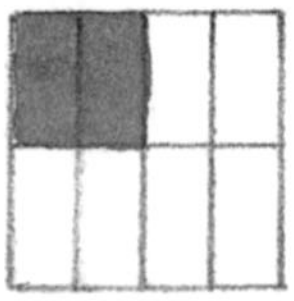 $\frac{\square}{8} = \frac{\square}{4}$

3 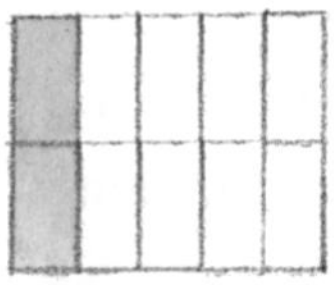 $\frac{\square}{10} = \frac{\square}{5}$

4 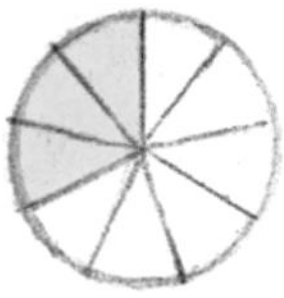 $\frac{\square}{9} = \frac{\square}{3}$

5 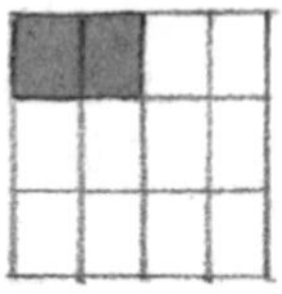 $\frac{\square}{12} = \frac{\square}{6}$

6 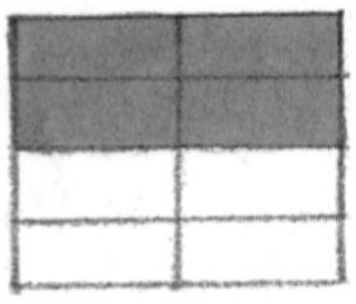 $\frac{\square}{4} = \frac{\square}{2}$

7 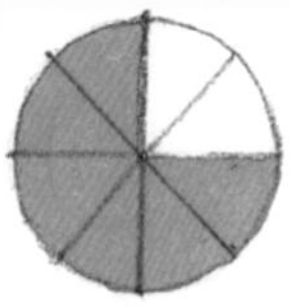 $\frac{6}{\square} = \frac{3}{\square}$

8 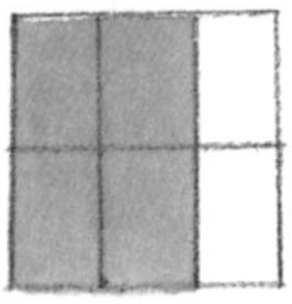 $\frac{4}{\square} = \frac{2}{\square}$

9 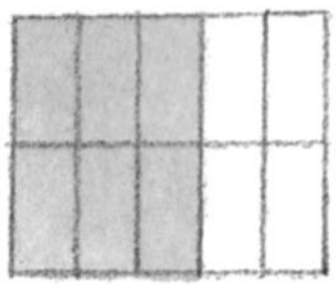 $\frac{6}{\square} = \frac{3}{\square}$

10 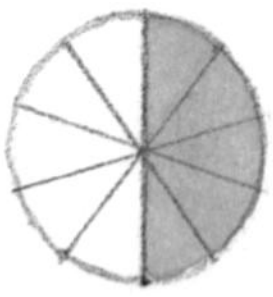 $\frac{5}{\square} = \frac{1}{\square}$

11 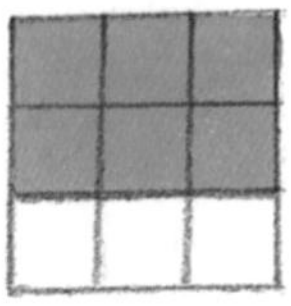 $\frac{6}{\square} = \frac{2}{\square}$

12 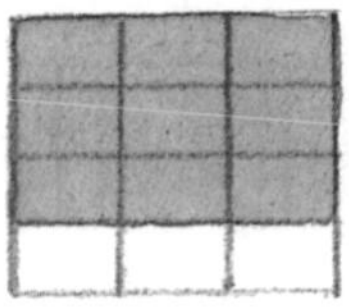 $\frac{9}{\square} = \frac{3}{\square}$

You're zippy! Have a scooter sticker.

Colour in your score.

Multiplication and division facts

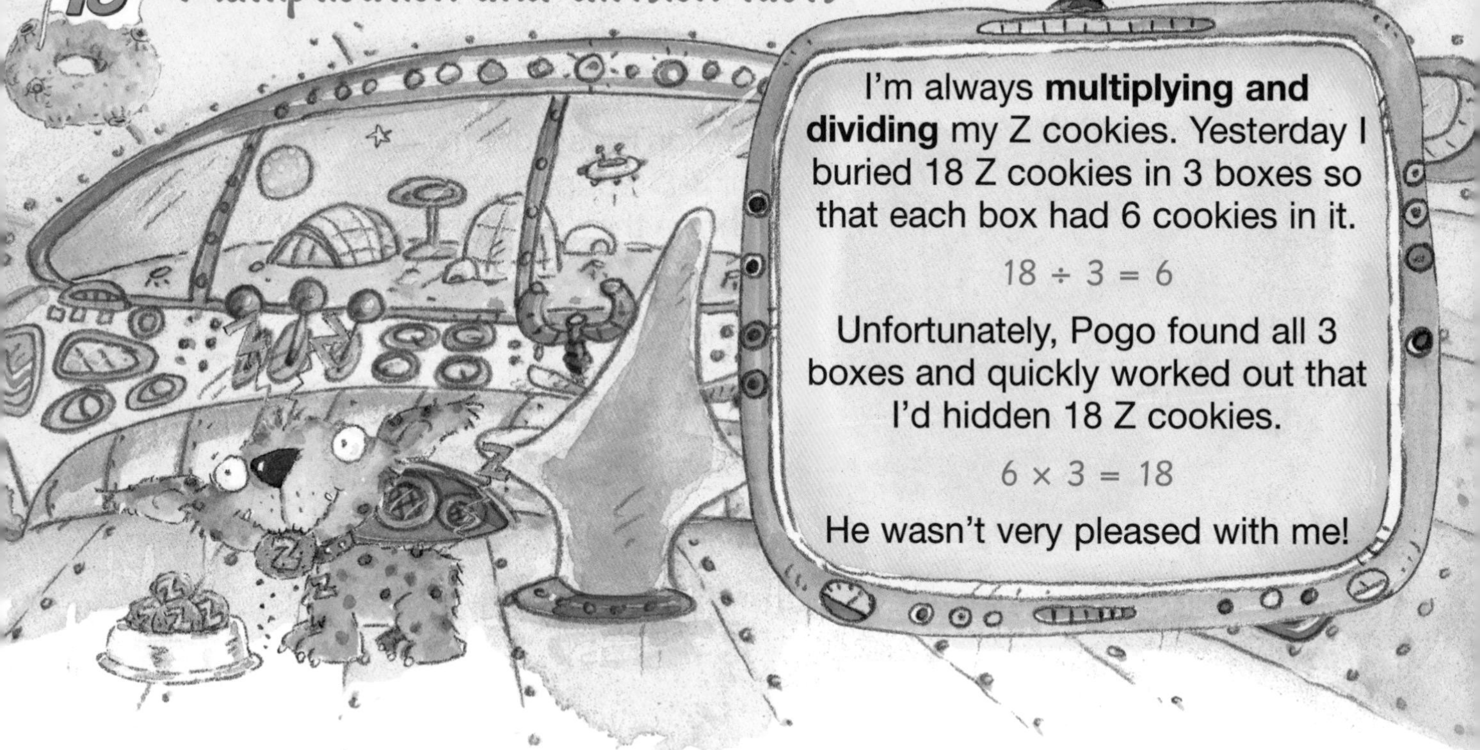

I'm always **multiplying and dividing** my Z cookies. Yesterday I buried 18 Z cookies in 3 boxes so that each box had 6 cookies in it.

$18 \div 3 = 6$

Unfortunately, Pogo found all 3 boxes and quickly worked out that I'd hidden 18 Z cookies.

$6 \times 3 = 18$

He wasn't very pleased with me!

Fill in the missing numbers. Time yourself to test your speed.

1 $6 \times \square = 30$

2 $9 \times 7 = \square$

3 $\square \times 4 = 32$

4 $5 \times 8 = \square$

5 $4 \times \square = 36$

6 $\square \times 3 = 24$

7 $21 \div 7 = \square$

8 $56 \div \square = 7$

9 $\square \div 6 = 4$

10 $81 \div 9 = \square$

11 $\square \div 4 = 8$

12 $45 \div \square = 5$

Good work! Have a Z cookie sticker.

Colour in your score.

TEST 11

3-D shapes

Mini T just told me that all **3-D shapes** have faces. I hope they're happy faces!
face
This cube has 6 faces.
Hurray! Come on, Mini T, let's dance!

Fill in the correct names for each shape.

1 

s _ _ _ _ e

2 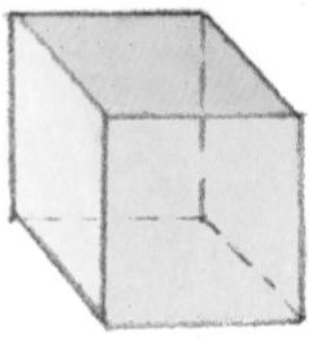

c _ _ _ _ _ d

3 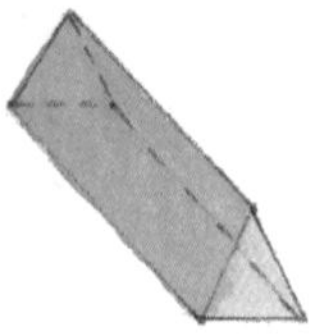

pr _ _ m

4 

c _ _ e

5 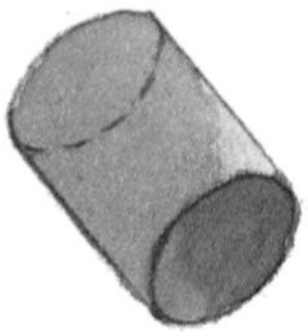

c _ _ _ _ _ _ _ r

6 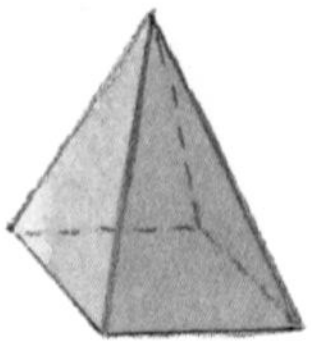

p _ _ _ _ _ _ d

Work out how many faces each shape has.

7 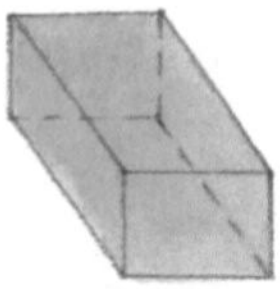 ☐

8  ☐

9 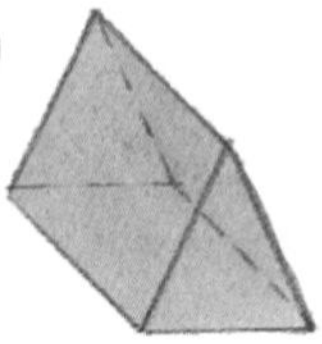 ☐

10  ☐

11 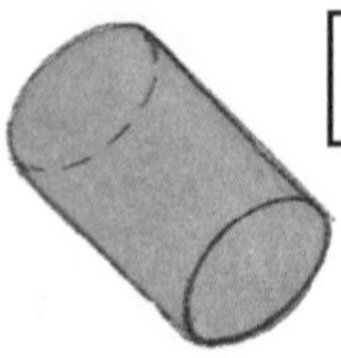 ☐

12  ☐

12
11
10
9
8
7
6
5
4
3
2
1

Well done! Have a Mini T sticker.

Colour in your score.

TEST 12

Reading the time

I like to have two watches for **reading the time.** The one with hands ticks in time with my music and my digital one has a stopwatch to see how long each song lasts.

Actually, they're good to look at together. Say the hour first and then count the minutes past the hour in 5s and then 1s. Check these two watches:

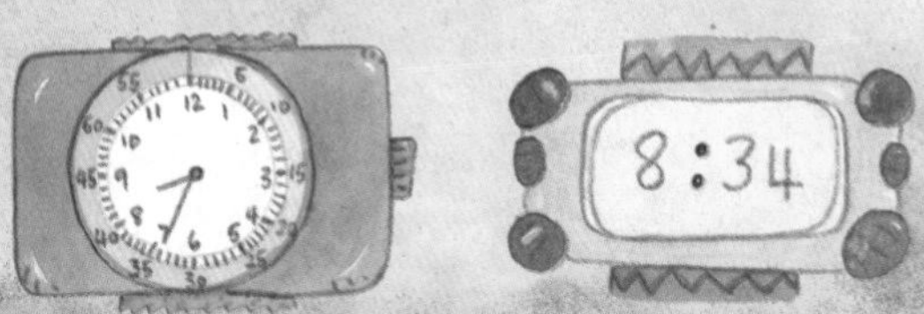

Work out the times shown on these watches.

1  ____________

2  ____________

3  ____________

4  ____________

5  ____________

6  ____________

7  ____________

8  ____________

9  ____________

10  ____________

11  ____________

12  ____________

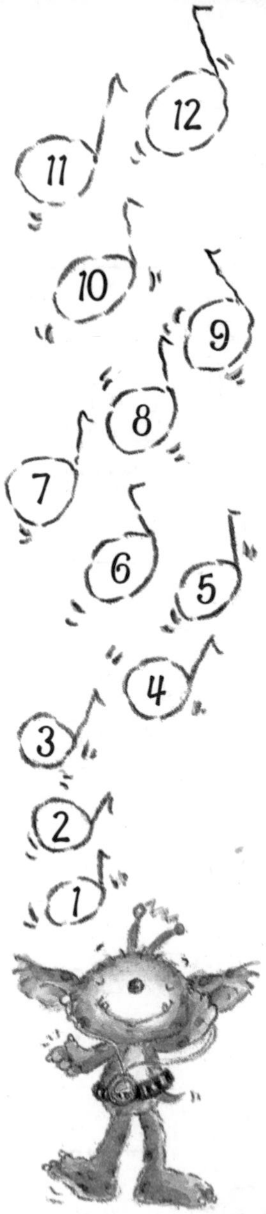

Easy! Have a musical sticker.

Colour in your score.

TEST 13 Written addition

I'm collecting football stickers and have filled up a whole book, which is 155 stickers. I've just counted my spare stickers and I've got another 67. So how many have I got altogether? Oh dear, this is tangling my antennae! I'd better write this down.

```
  155
+  67
-----
  222
-----
   11
```

5 + 7 is 12, so I write the 2 in the answer space and write the 1 under the tens numbers, so I don't forget. 50 + 60 + 10 is 120, so I write the 2 in the answer space and put the 1 under the hundreds numbers.

100 + 100 is 200. So I've got 222 altogether. He shoots, he scores!

Work out the answers to these.

1. 117 + 58 = ____
2. 128 + 64 = ____
3. 185 + 56 = ____
4. 219 + 45 = ____
5. 204 + 88 = ____
6. 176 + 67 = ____
7. 394 + 68 = ____
8. 438 + 59 = ____
9. 545 + 86 = ____
10. 367 + 57 = ____
11. 528 + 83 = ____
12. 676 + 96 = ____

Goal! Have a football sticker.

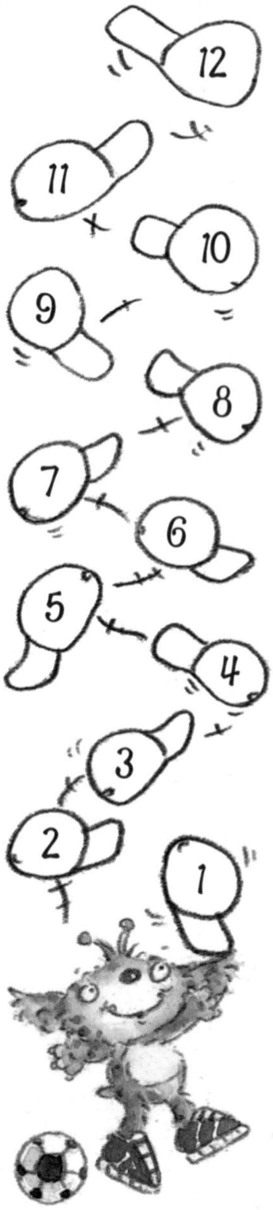

Colour in your score.

Ready, steady, bounce! I would love to bounce 10 times higher than I can, or even 100 times or 1000 times higher. I can bounce 25 metres in the air, so how high would that be?

	×10	×100	×1000
25	250	2500	25 000

Look at this – dividing is the opposite of multiplying:

	÷10	÷100	÷1000
25 000	2500	250	25

That brings me back to earth!

Work out the numbers coming out of each machine.

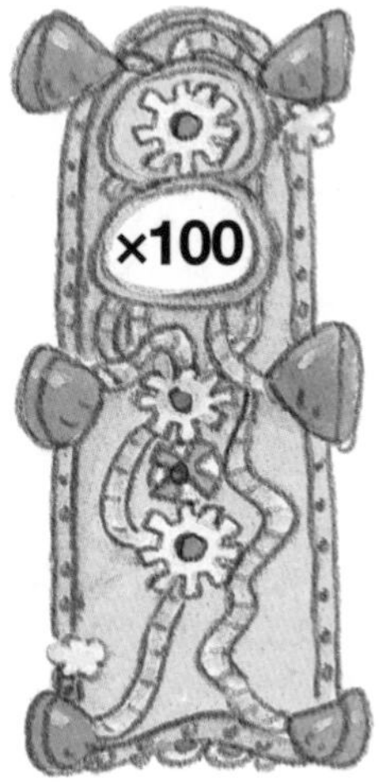

1 89 ×100

2 156

3 395

4 19 ×1000

5 78

6 124

7 3400 ÷10

8 950

9 3670

10 1400 ÷100

11 3600

12 9300

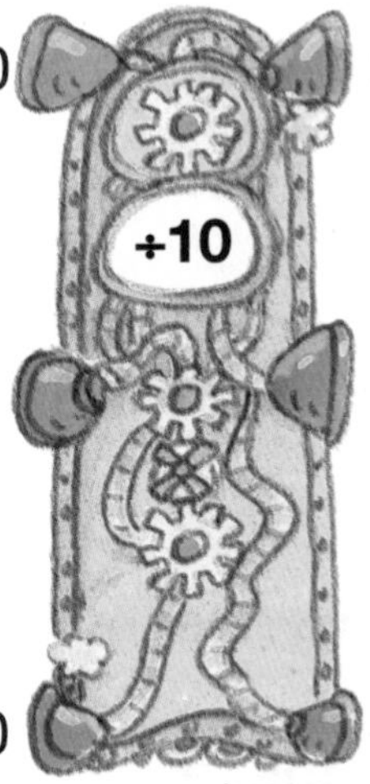

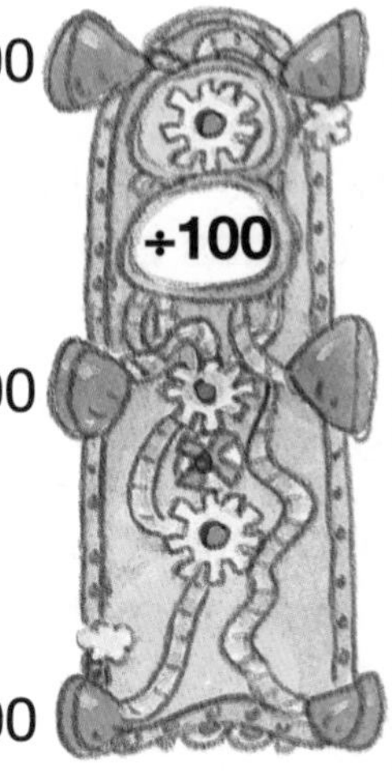

Tables and graphs

Pogo has made two charts of my Z cookie eating habits! Can you help me read them?

Table

Flavour	Z	Nut	Oat
Week 1	65	35	40
Week 2	35	70	35
Week 3	45	45	50
Week 4	70	25	45

Graph

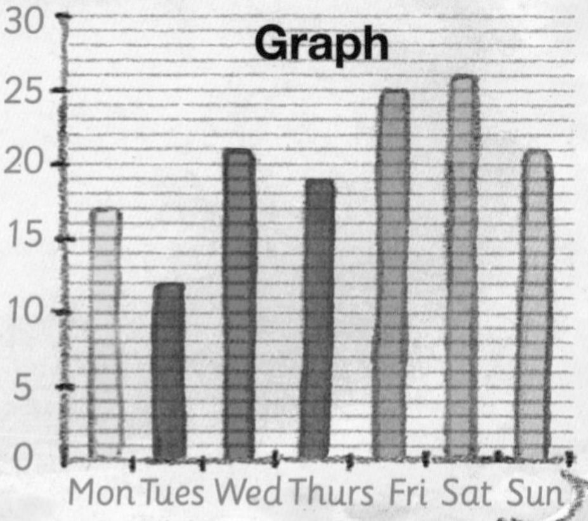

Use the graph to answer these.

1 On which day did I eat the most cookies? __________

2 How many did I eat on Thursday? __________

3 On which two days did I eat the same number? __________ __________

4 How many more did I eat on Friday than Tuesday? __________

5 On which day did I eat 25 cookies? __________

6 How many did I eat altogether at the weekend? __________

Use the table to answer these.

7 How many Z cookies were bought in Week 3? __________

8 In which week were the most nut cookies bought? __________

9 In which week was the same number of Z cookies and oat cookies bought? __________

10 How many more Z cookies than nut cookies were bought in Week 1? __________

11 In which week was double the number of nut cookies bought than the other flavours? __________

12 How many biscuits were bought in total each week? __________

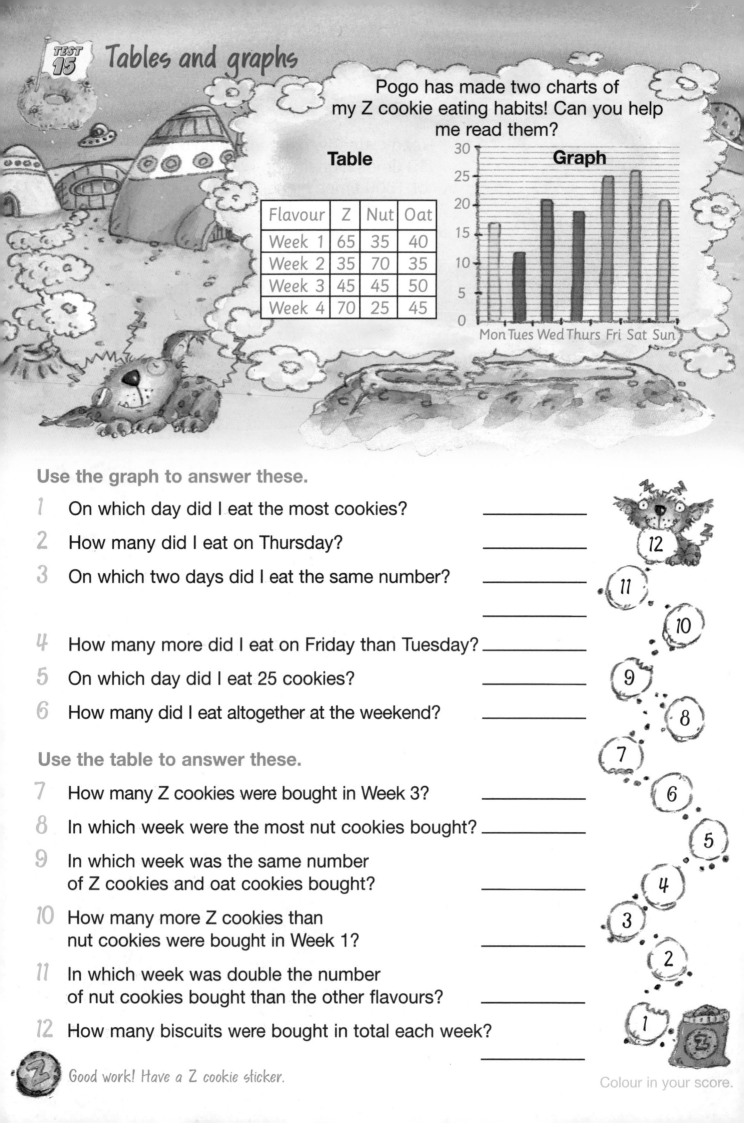

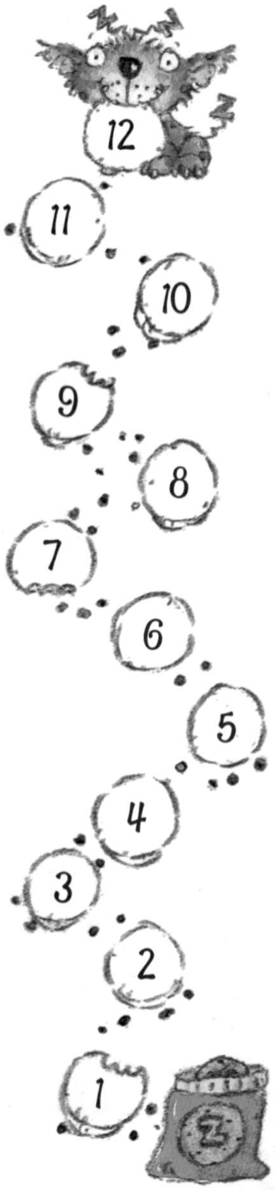

Good work! Have a Z cookie sticker.

Colour in your score.

TEST 16

Coordinates

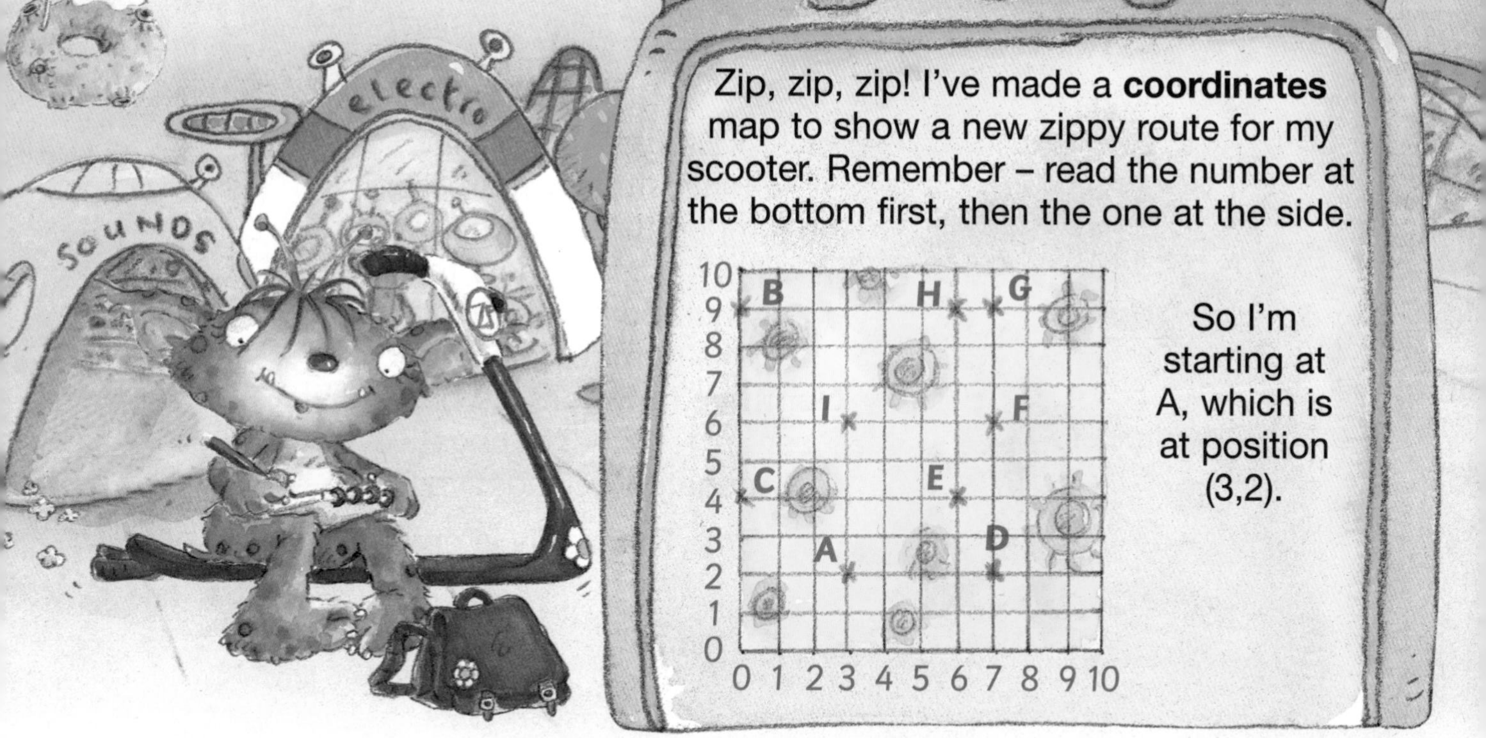

electro
SOUNDS
Zip, zip, zip! I've made a **coordinates** map to show a new zippy route for my scooter. Remember – read the number at the bottom first, then the one at the side.
So I'm starting at A, which is at position (3,2).
B
H
G
I
F
C
E
A
D
0 1 2 3 4 5 6 7 8 9 10
0 1 2 3 4 5 6 7 8 9 10

Work out which letters are at the following coordinates.

1 (7,6) ________

2 (6,9) ________

3 (0,9) ________

4 (3,6) ________

Work out the coordinates for the following letters.

5 D ________

6 C ________

7 G ________

8 E ________

Name the shapes made if you join these coordinates.

9 (3,2) (3,6) (7,6) (7,2)

____

10 (0,4) (6,4) (6,9)

____

11 (3,2) (6,4) (3,6) (0,4)

____

12 (0,4) (6,4) (6,9) (0,9)

____

Colour in your score.

You're zippy! Have a scooter sticker.

TEST 17 Negative numbers

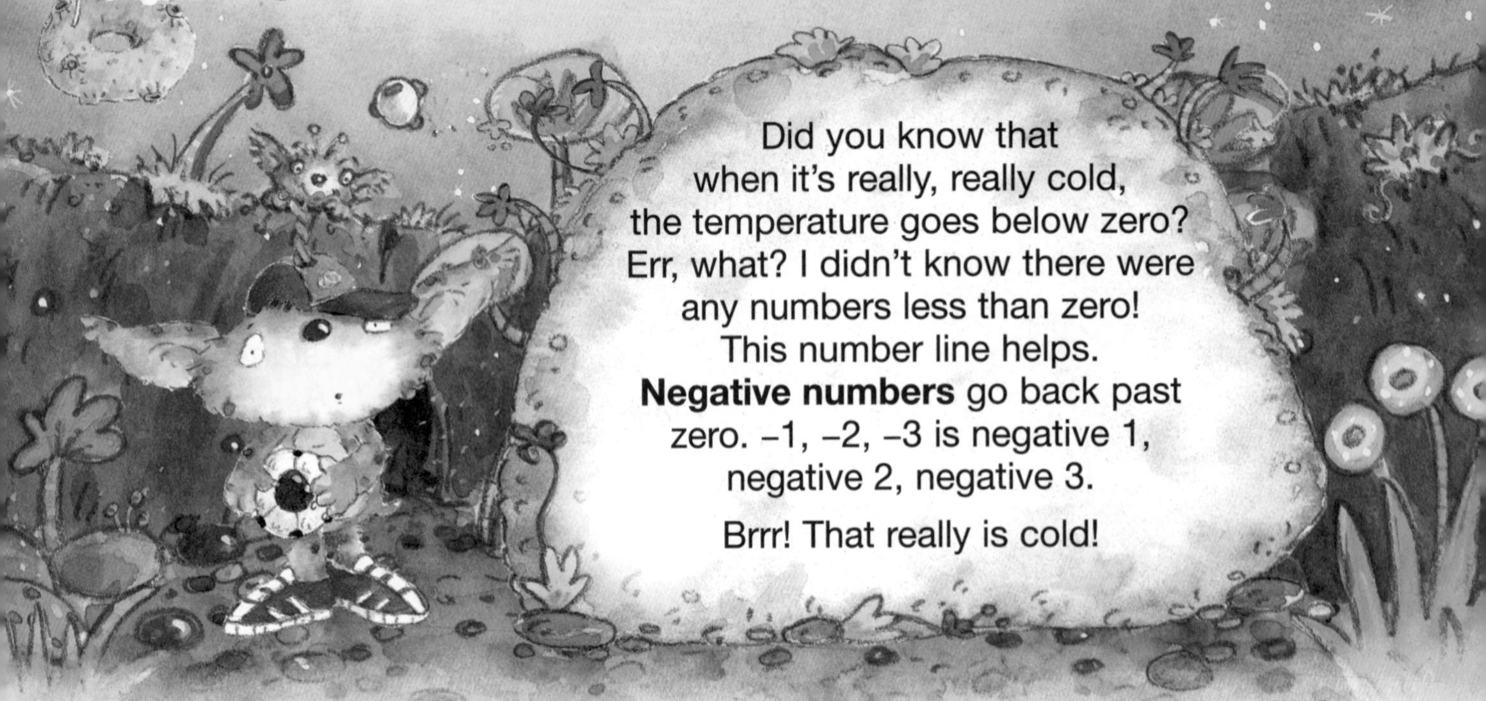
Did you know that
when it's really, really cold,
the temperature goes below zero?
Err, what? I didn't know there were
any numbers less than zero!
This number line helps.
Negative numbers go back past
zero. –1, –2, –3 is negative 1,
negative 2, negative 3.
Brrr! That really is cold!

–10	–9	–8	–7	–6	–5	–4	–3	–2	–1	0	1	2	3	4	5	6	7	8	9	10

Fill in the missing numbers, using the number line above to help you.

		1	2		3		4					
–6	–5			–2		0		2	3	4	5	6

5	6			7		8		
		–6	–5		–3		–1	0

	9			10						
–10		–8	–7		–5	–4	–3	–2	–1	0

11	12							
		–2	–1	0	1	2	3	4	5

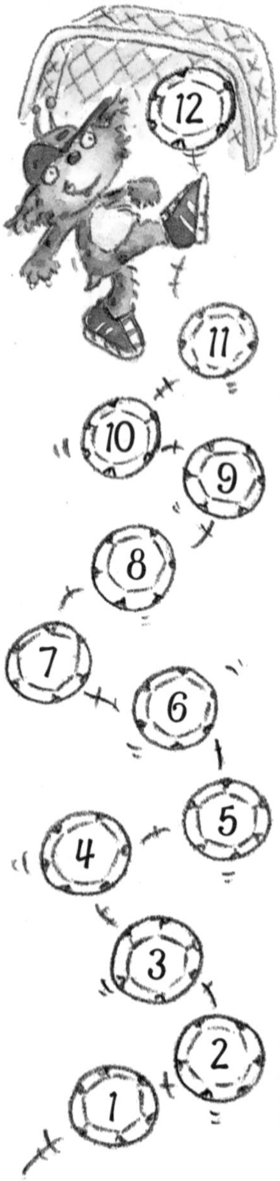

Colour in your score.

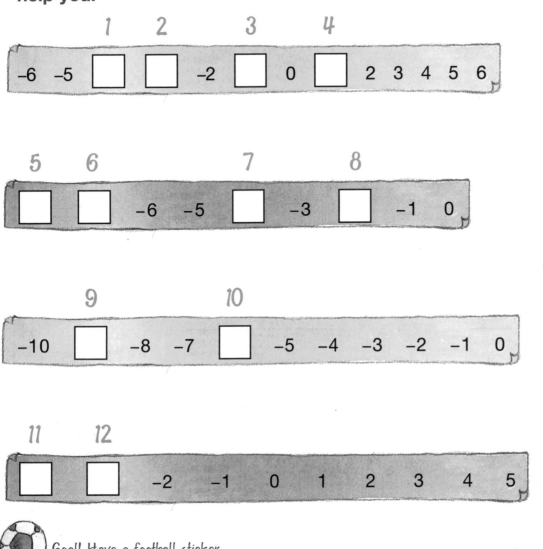

Goal! Have a football sticker.

TEST 18 Fractions and decimals

Boing, boing, boing! Decimals are types of fractions, but with a bit more point to them! For instance.

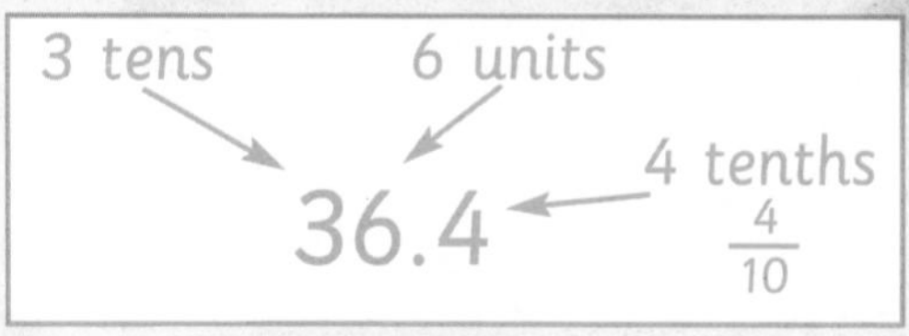

Just learn the tenths and they're easy.

$$\frac{1}{10} = 0.1$$
$$\frac{2}{10} = 0.2$$
$$\frac{5}{10} = \frac{1}{2} = 0.5$$

Ready, steady, bounce!

Write these fractions as decimals.

1 $\frac{3}{10}$ = ____________

2 $\frac{6}{10}$ = ____________

3 $4\frac{9}{10}$ = ____________

4 $8\frac{4}{10}$ = ____________

5 $19\frac{8}{10}$ = ____________

6 $32\frac{7}{10}$ = ____________

Write these decimals as fractions.

7 0.8 = ____________

8 0.5 = ____________

9 7.3 = ____________

10 9.1 = ____________

11 24.6 = ____________

12 41.2 = ____________

Put a spring in your step! Have a springy sticker.

Colour in your score.

TEST 19 Fractions of quantities

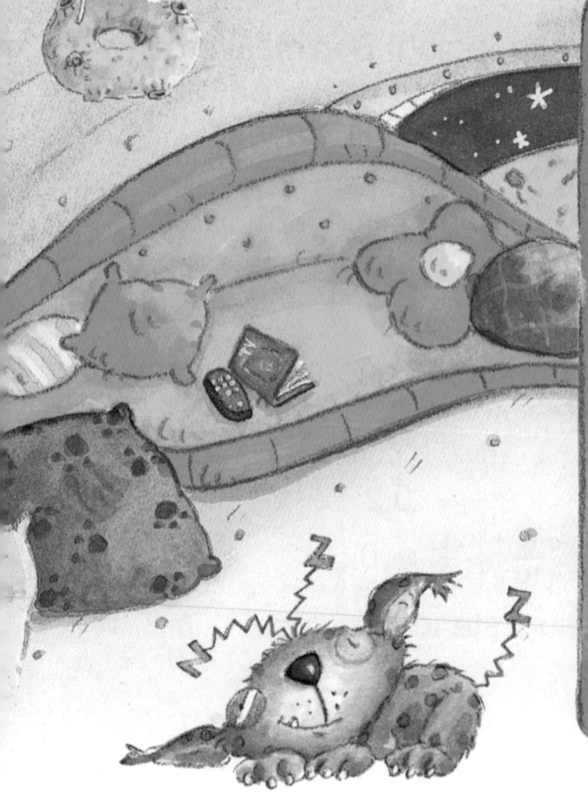

This Z cookie box holds 12 cookies, but I've eaten $\frac{3}{4}$ of them. I worked that out because I know that $\frac{1}{4}$ of 12 is the same as $12 \div 4 = 3$. So there's $\frac{1}{4}$ of the box left. I've eaten 3 times that, which means that three-quarters of 12 is 9.

$$\frac{3}{4} \text{ of } 12 = 9$$

Divide 12 by 4 and then multiply by 3!

Easy! You could do this in your... zzz.

Work out the answers to these.

1 $\frac{1}{4}$ of 20 = ☐

2 $\frac{3}{4}$ of 20 = ☐

3 $\frac{1}{3}$ of 12 = ☐

4 $\frac{2}{3}$ of 12 = ☐

5 $\frac{1}{10}$ of 70 = ☐

6 $\frac{3}{10}$ of 70 = ☐

7 $\frac{1}{5}$ of 30 = ☐

8 $\frac{4}{5}$ of 30 = ☐

9 $\frac{1}{4}$ of 40 = ☐

10 $\frac{3}{4}$ of 40 = ☐

11 $\frac{1}{6}$ of 18 = ☐

12 $\frac{5}{6}$ of 18 = ☐

Good work! Have a Z cookie sticker.

Colour in your score.

TEST 20

Multiples

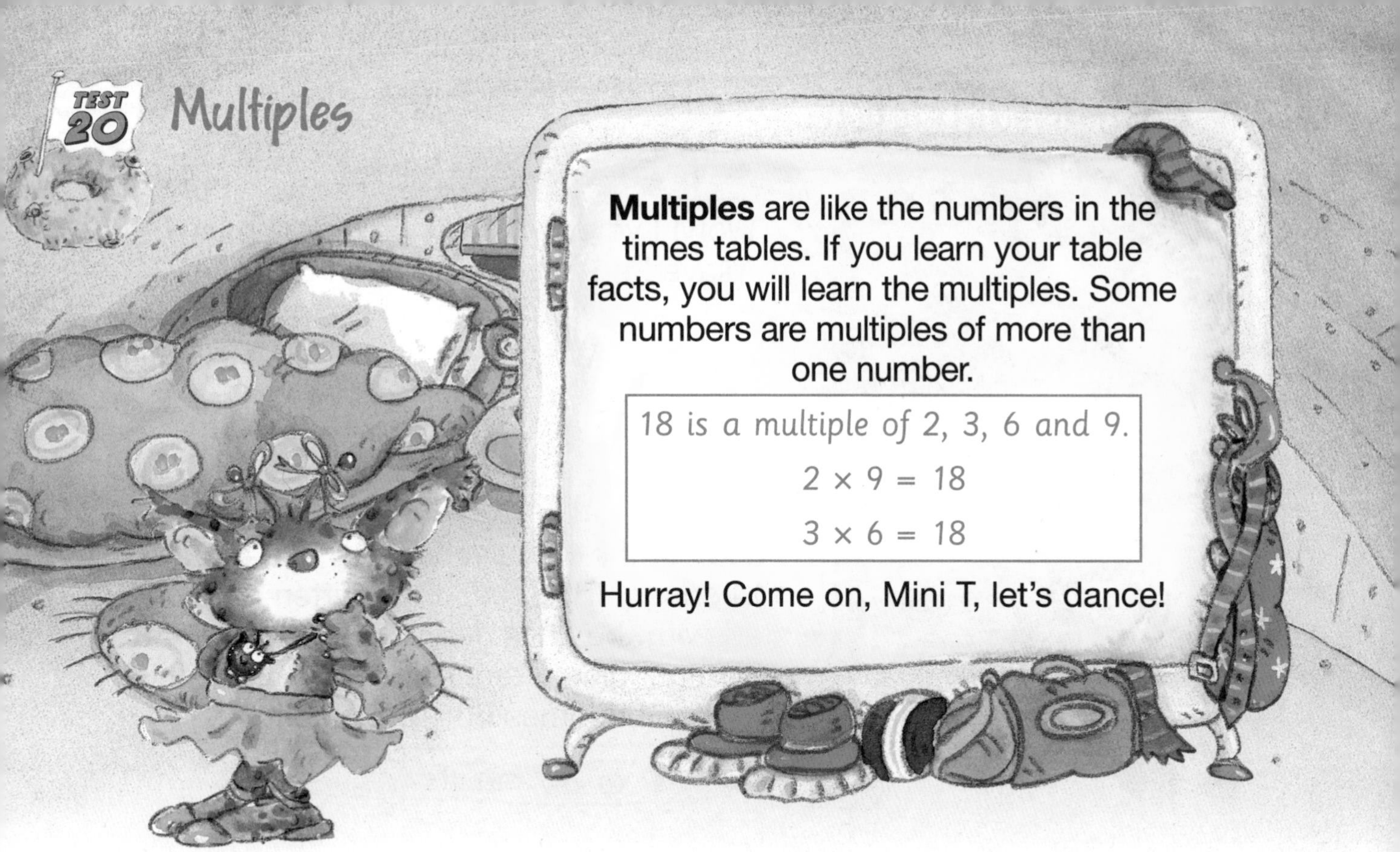

Multiples are like the numbers in the times tables. If you learn your table facts, you will learn the multiples. Some numbers are multiples of more than one number.

18 is a multiple of 2, 3, 6 and 9.
2 × 9 = 18
3 × 6 = 18

Hurray! Come on, Mini T, let's dance!

Write the numbers below in the correct toy boxes. Some of the numbers will belong in more than one box.

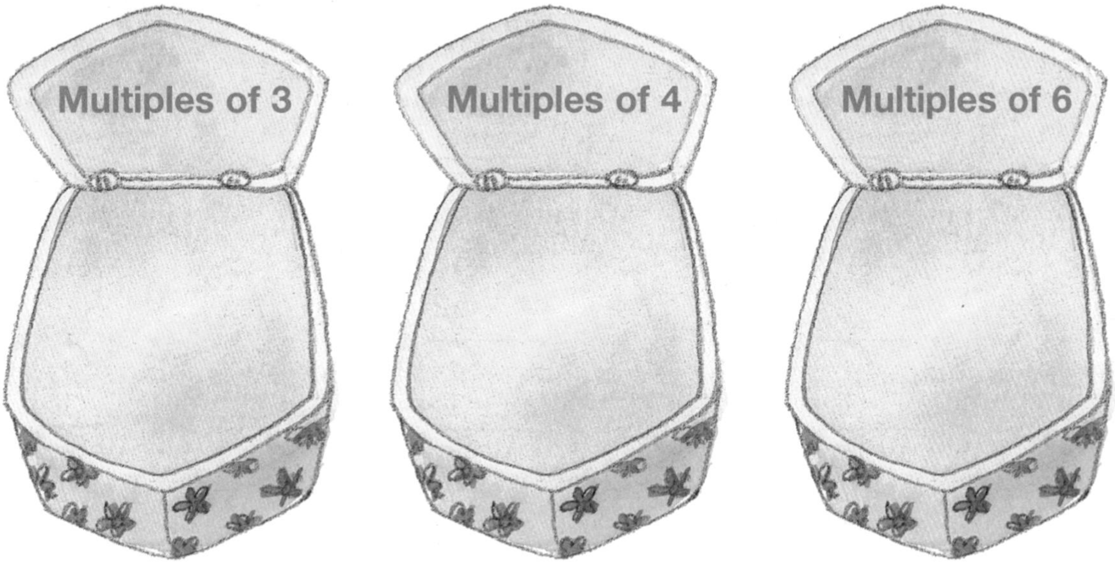

1 21

2 18

3 40

4 24

5 42

6 32

7 27

8 48

9 66

10 60

11 72

12 64

Colour in your score.

Well done! Have a Mini T sticker.

Wow! I've got 172 songs on my music player! If I cut 58 of them, how many would I have left?

$$
\begin{array}{r}
1\,{}^6\!\!\not7\,{}^1\!2 \\
-\ 5\ 8 \\
\hline
1\ 1\ 4
\end{array}
$$

Look at the way I've worked this out as 114 songs. If you use this written method, start with the units. Make 2 – 8 into 12 – 8 by exchanging a ten from the 70, then this becomes 60 – 50. Cool!

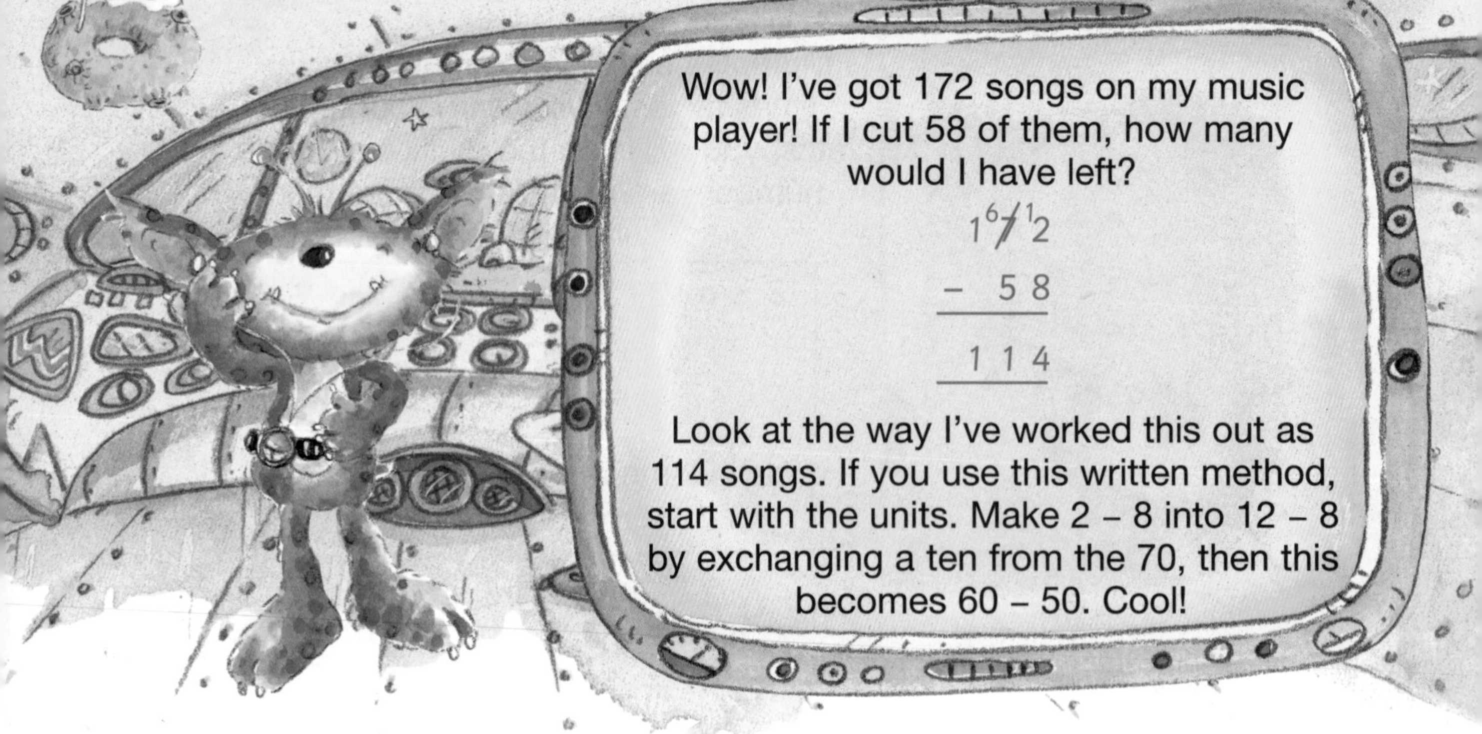

Work out the answers to these.

1
```
   147
-   39
_____
```

2
```
   152
-   35
_____
```

3
```
   164
-   46
_____
```

4
```
   142
-   38
_____
```

5
```
   171
-   57
_____
```

6
```
   165
-   52
_____
```

7
```
   126
-   67
_____
```

8
```
   113
-   56
_____
```

9
```
   152
-   73
_____
```

10
```
   164
-   75
_____
```

11
```
   137
-   59
_____
```

12
```
   172
-   88
_____
```

Easy! Have a musical sticker.

Colour in your score.

TEST 22

Rounding and approximate answers

We **round** numbers to make them easier to work with. I do it by bouncing the numbers up to the next ten if they are halfway or more and bouncing down if they are below halfway. If you round numbers, you can work out **approximate** or rough answers.

Rounding to the nearest **10**:

70 71 72 73 74 **75** 76 77 78 79 **80**

73 + 78 is approximately 70 + 80 = 150

Rounding to the nearest **100**:

800 810 820 830 840 **850** 860 870 880 890 **900**

823 + 819 is approximately 800 + 800 = 1600

Round these numbers to the nearest 10 to work out the approximate answers.

1 48 + 67 ☐

2 93 + 71 ☐

3 124 + 97 ☐

4 138 – 62 ☐

5 153 – 79 ☐

6 166 – 97 ☐

Round these numbers to the nearest 100 to work out the approximate answers.

7 423 + 384 ☐

8 956 + 439 ☐

9 839 + 666 ☐

10 1224 – 309 ☐

11 1099 – 648 ☐

12 1754 – 861 ☐

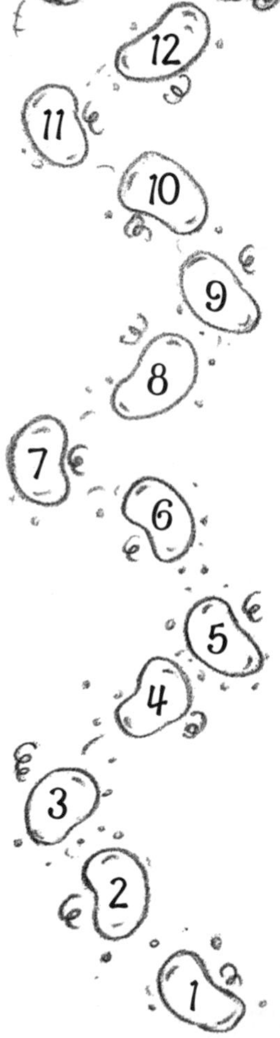

Colour in your score.

Put a spring in your step! Have a springy sticker.

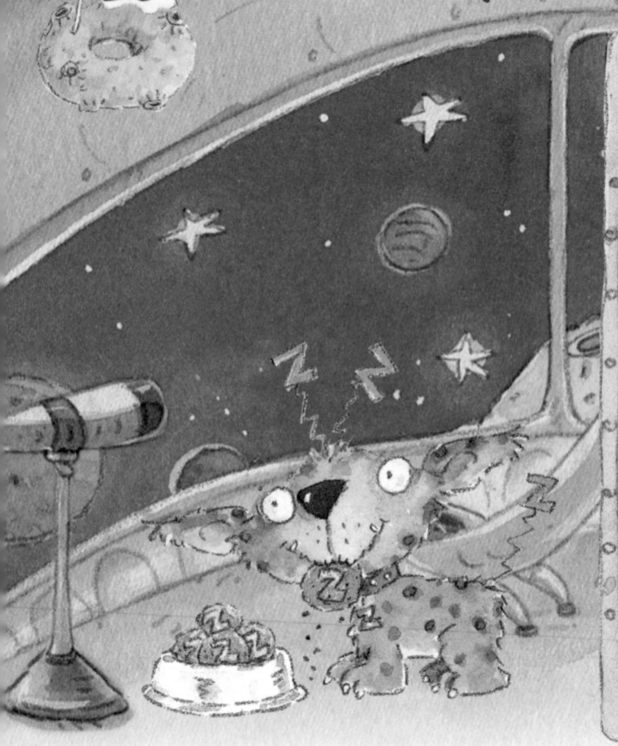

☆ I've just broken my record by eating 52 Z cookies in one day! If Pogo gave me that amount each day, that would be over 1000 cookies in a week! Let me just check that...

$$
\begin{array}{r}
52 \\
\times\ 7 \\
\hline
14 \\
\hline
350 \\
\hline
364 \\
\end{array}
$$

$2 \times 7 = 14$

$50 \times 7 = 350$

$350 + 14 = 364$

364 cookies... is that all? I thought I was looking a bit skinny!

Work out the answers to these.

1
$$
\begin{array}{r}
27 \\
\times\ 3 \\
\hline
\end{array}
$$

2
$$
\begin{array}{r}
39 \\
\times\ 6 \\
\hline
\end{array}
$$

3
$$
\begin{array}{r}
53 \\
\times\ 4 \\
\hline
\end{array}
$$

4
$$
\begin{array}{r}
67 \\
\times\ 5 \\
\hline
\end{array}
$$

5
$$
\begin{array}{r}
82 \\
\times\ 6 \\
\hline
\end{array}
$$

6
$$
\begin{array}{r}
65 \\
\times\ 7 \\
\hline
\end{array}
$$

7
$$
\begin{array}{r}
76 \\
\times\ 4 \\
\hline
\end{array}
$$

8
$$
\begin{array}{r}
49 \\
\times\ 9 \\
\hline
\end{array}
$$

9
$$
\begin{array}{r}
84 \\
\times\ 5 \\
\hline
\end{array}
$$

10
$$
\begin{array}{r}
38 \\
\times\ 8 \\
\hline
\end{array}
$$

11
$$
\begin{array}{r}
94 \\
\times\ 3 \\
\hline
\end{array}
$$

12
$$
\begin{array}{r}
53 \\
\times\ 7 \\
\hline
\end{array}
$$

12 11 10 9 8 7 6 5 4 3 2 1

Good work! Have a Z cookie sticker.

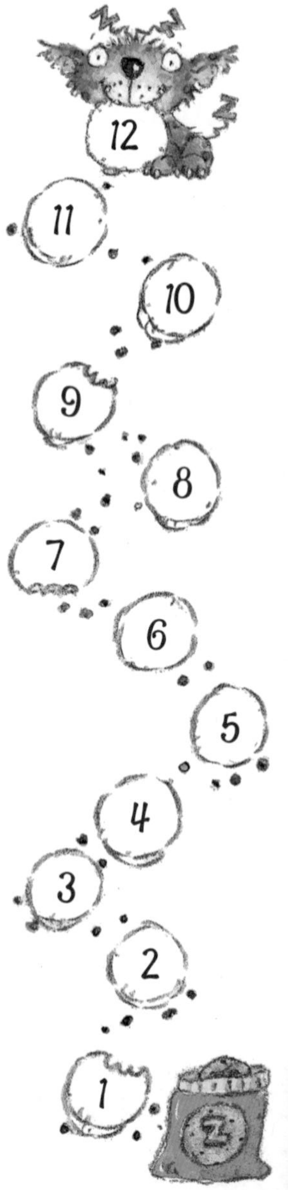

Colour in your score.

TEST 24

Angles

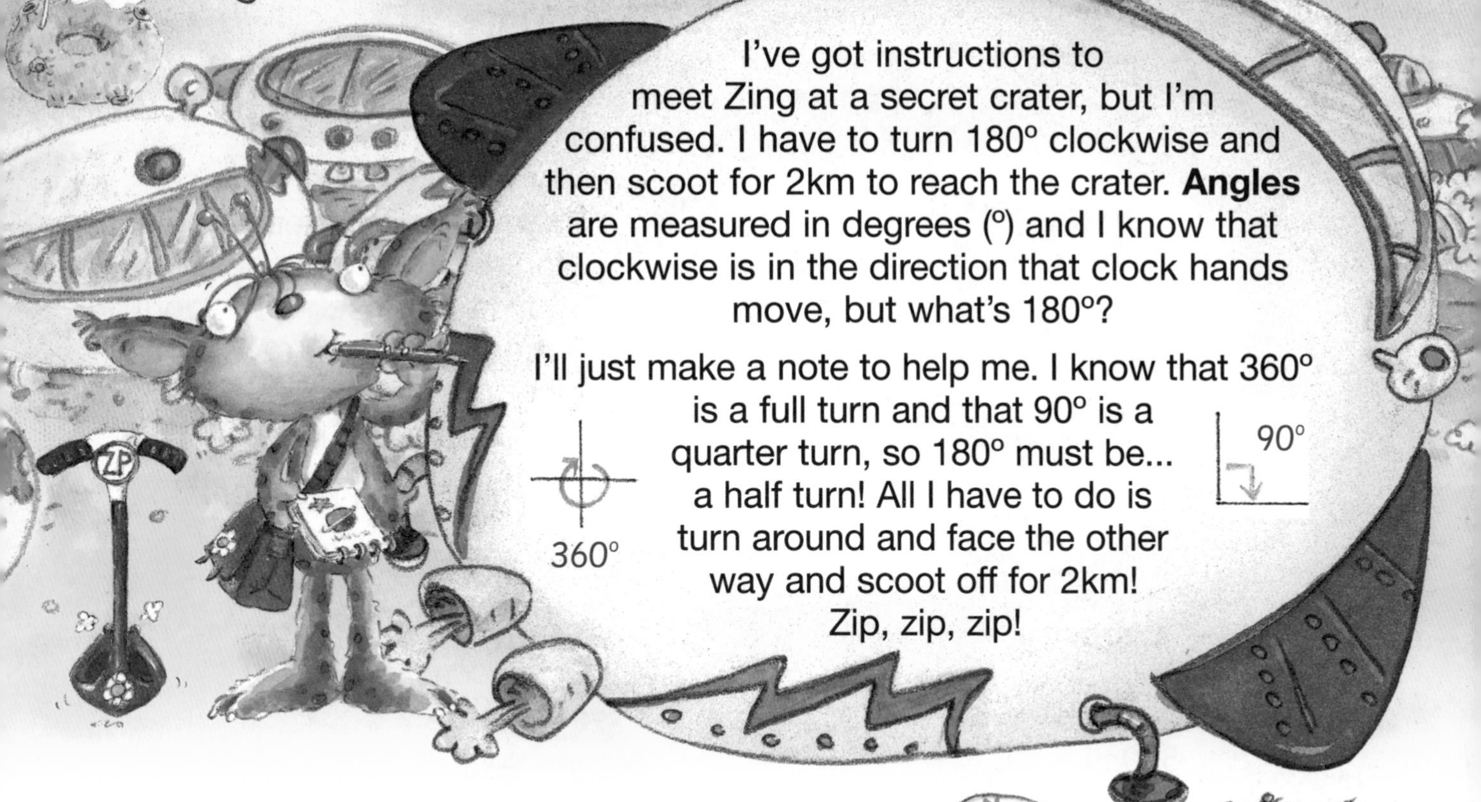
I've got instructions to meet Zing at a secret crater, but I'm confused. I have to turn 180° clockwise and then scoot for 2km to reach the crater. **Angles** are measured in degrees (°) and I know that clockwise is in the direction that clock hands move, but what's 180°?
I'll just make a note to help me. I know that 360° is a full turn and that 90° is a quarter turn, so 180° must be... a half turn! All I have to do is turn around and face the other way and scoot off for 2km! Zip, zip, zip!
360°
90°
ZP

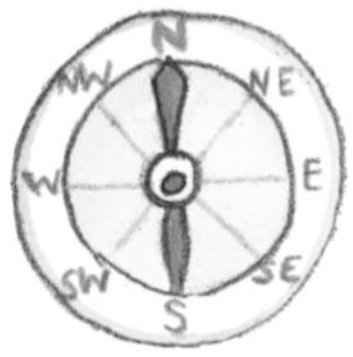

This compass shows eight directions. Write the directions you will face after these turns.

1 Face north. Turn 90° clockwise. ____________

2 Face east. Turn 360° anticlockwise. ____________

3 Face north. Turn 180° anticlockwise. ____________

4 Face south. Turn 90° anticlockwise. ____________

5 Face west. Turn 90° clockwise. ____________

6 Face east. Turn 90° anticlockwise. ____________

7 Face south. Turn 360° clockwise. ____________

8 Face north-east. Turn 90° clockwise. ____________

9 Face north-west. Turn 180° anticlockwise. ____________

10 Face south-east. Turn 360° anticlockwise. ____________

11 Face north-east. Turn 180° clockwise. ____________

12 Face south-west. Turn 90° anticlockwise. ____________

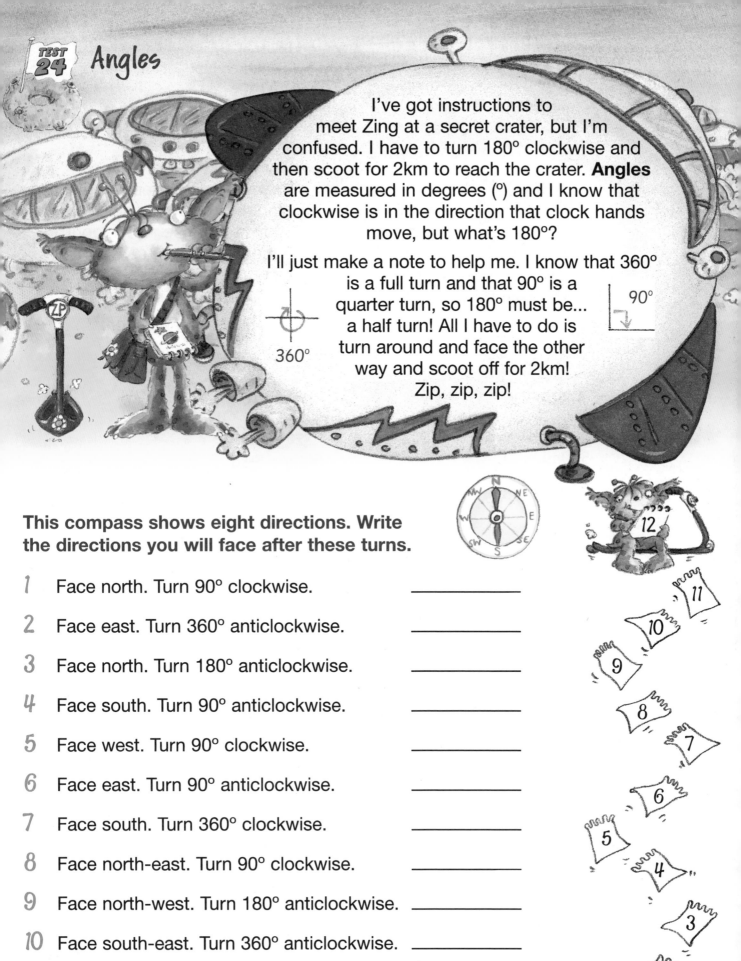

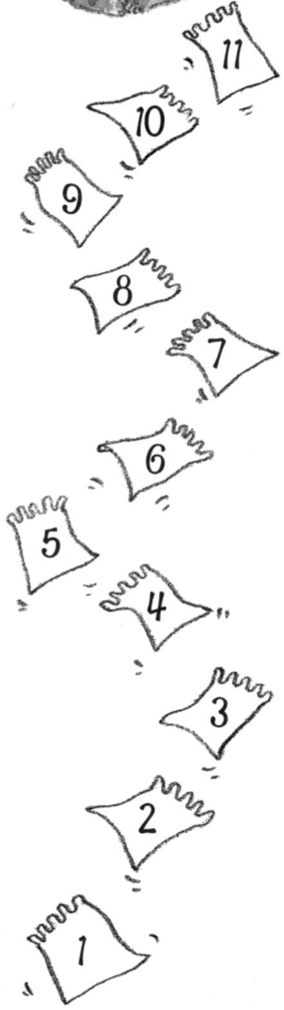

You're zippy! Have a scooter sticker.

Colour in your score.

TEST 25

Measures

electro
MODE
SOUNDS
Err, what? There are so many zeros in measuring, it tangles my antennae! Zing gave me these facts about **measures**, so I can learn them quickly and get back to playing football!
He shoots, he scores!

Capacity

1000 millilitres (ml) = 1 litre (l)

500ml = $\frac{1}{2}$l

250ml = $\frac{1}{4}$l

750ml = $\frac{3}{4}$l

Weight

1000 grams (g) = 1 kilogram (kg)

500g = $\frac{1}{2}$kg

250g = $\frac{1}{4}$kg

750g = $\frac{3}{4}$kg

Length

10 millimetres (mm) = 1 centimetre (cm)

100cm = 1 metre (m)

50cm = $\frac{1}{2}$m   25cm = $\frac{1}{4}$m   75cm = $\frac{3}{4}$m

1000m = 1 kilometre (km)

Write the equivalent units of measure.

1 3000g = ☐ kg

2 150cm = ☐ m

3 4l = ☐ ml

4 $2\frac{1}{2}$km = ☐ m

5 80mm = ☐ cm

6 275cm = ☐ m

7 $4\frac{1}{4}$kg = ☐ g

8 3750ml = ☐ l

9 $5\frac{1}{2}$m = ☐ cm

10 2250g = ☐ kg

11 9cm = ☐ mm

12 6750m = ☐ km

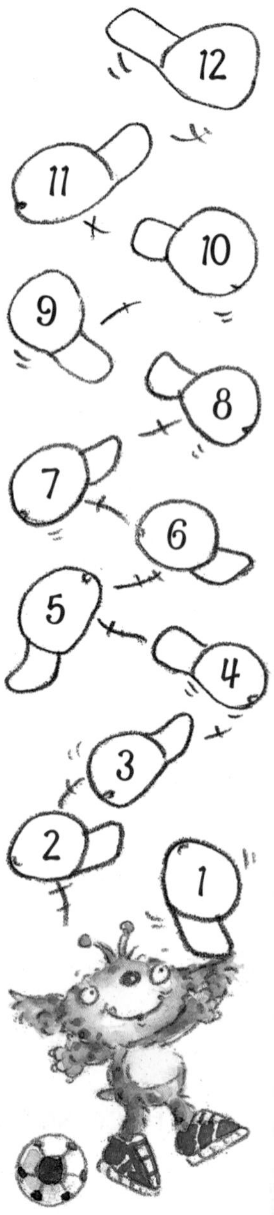

Colour in your score.

Goal! Have a football sticker.

TEST 26

Proportion

Boing, boing, boing!
I've just collected 12 bottles for recycling and 1 in every 3 of them is a plastic bottle.
This means the **proportion** is 1 in 3 or $\frac{1}{3}$, just like the fraction, one-third. So if I collected 30 bottles, then 10 would be plastic, or if I collected 300, then 100 would be plastic. Better get collecting, then!
Ready, steady, bounce!

Write the proportion of each shape chain that is red.

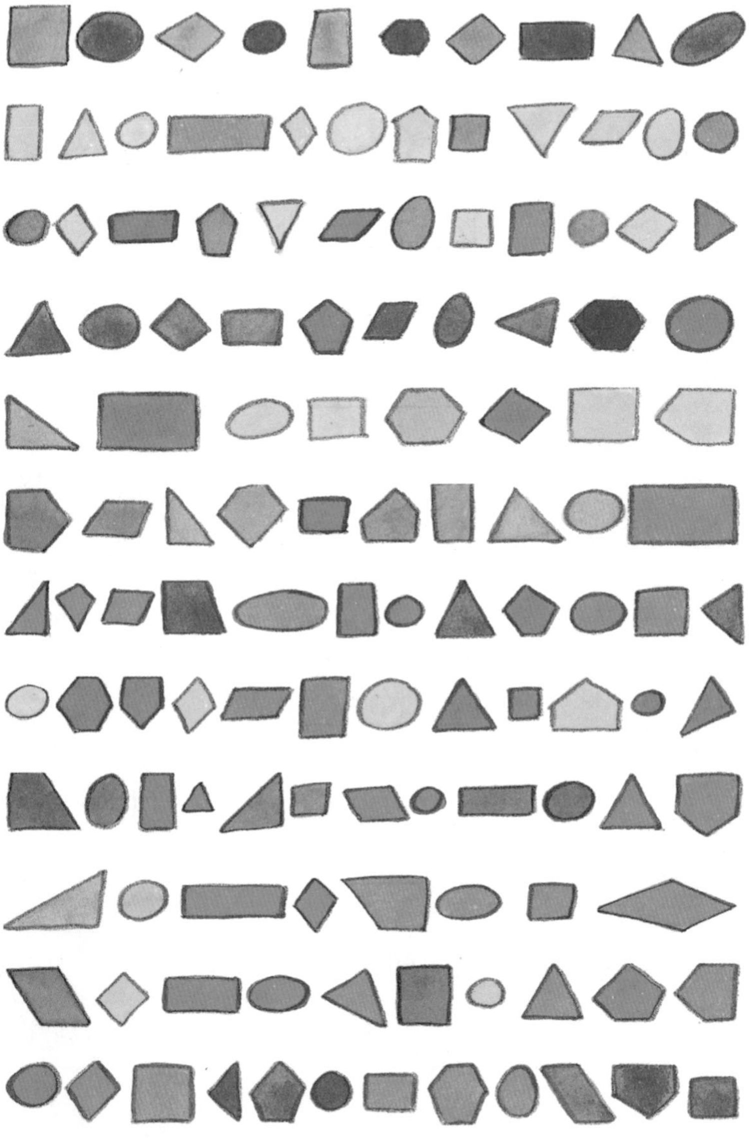

1 ☐
2 ☐
3 ☐
4 ☐
5 ☐
6 ☐
7 ☐
8 ☐
9 ☐
10 ☐
11 ☐
12 ☐

Put a spring in your step! Have a springy sticker.

Colour in your score.

TEST 27 Written division

I've got 42 beads and I need to put an equal number on three necklaces. Oh dear, Mini T, this is a tricky one! I need to work out 42 ÷ 3 to find out how many beads will be on each necklace.

$$42 \div 3 = (30 + 12) \div 3$$
$$= (30 \div 3) + (12 \div 3)$$
$$= 10 + 4$$
$$= 14$$

So that means each necklace will have 14 beads on it. Hurray! Come on, Mini T, let's dance!

Work out the answers to these.

1 85 ÷ 5 = ☐

2 78 ÷ 3 = ☐

3 72 ÷ 6 = ☐

4 56 ÷ 4 = ☐

5 69 ÷ 3 = ☐

6 90 ÷ 5 = ☐

7 96 ÷ 8 = ☐

8 84 ÷ 6 = ☐

9 87 ÷ 3 = ☐

10 76 ÷ 4 = ☐

11 91 ÷ 7 = ☐

12 96 ÷ 4 = ☐

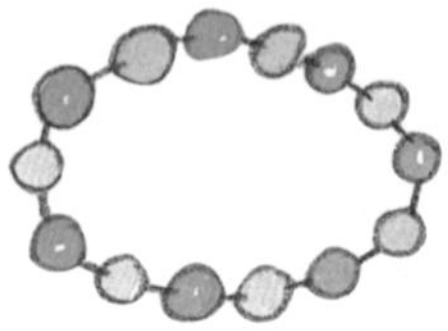

Hurray! Have a Mini T sticker.

Colour in your score.

TEST 28

Reading scales

Did you know that **scales** for measuring are just like number lines, except they show amounts? Just remember to look at the numbers that are on the scales and then work out what each marker on the line stands for.

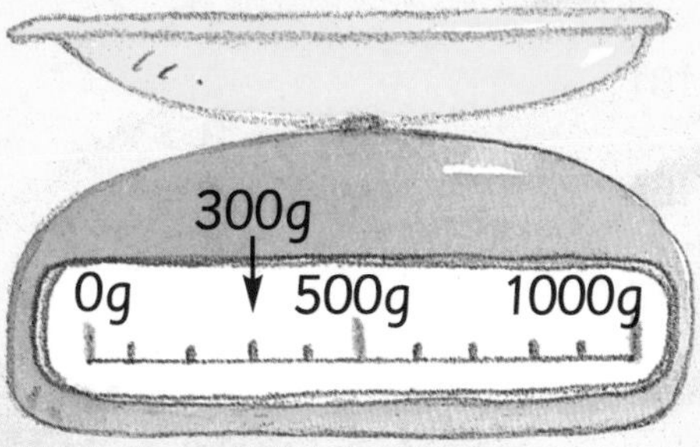

300g
0g
500g
1000g

See? Easy!

Write the amounts shown by each arrow.

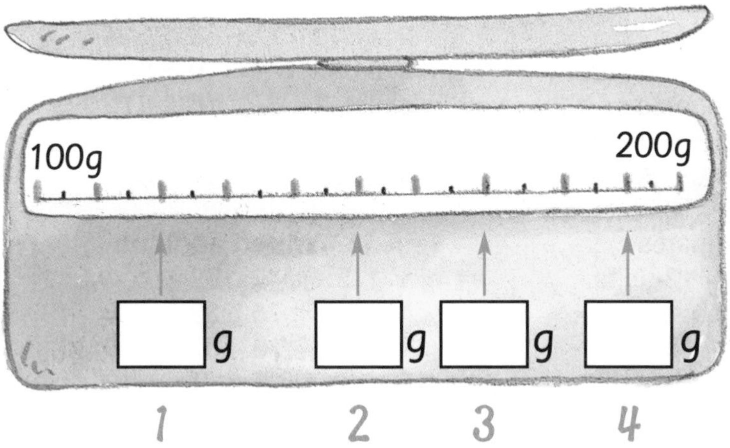

100g
200g
g
g
g
g
1
2
3
4

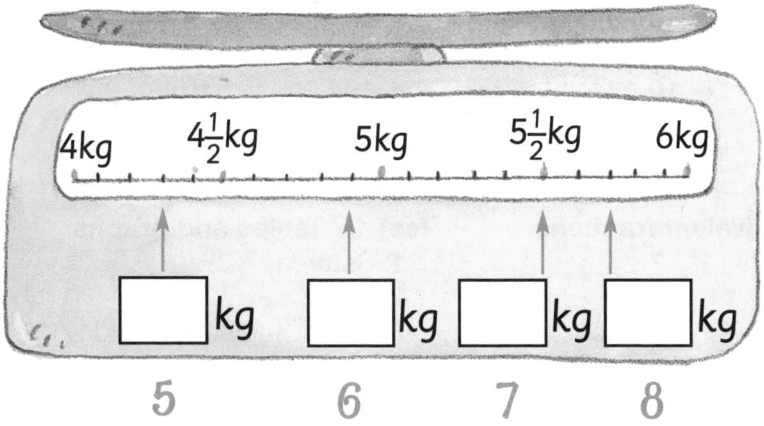

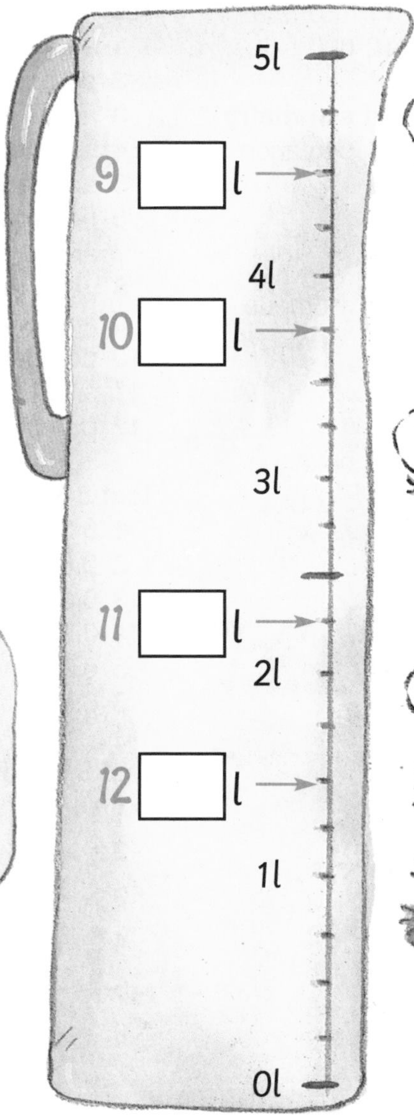

5l
9 l
4l
10 l
3l
11 l
2l
12 l
1l
0l

Congratulations! Have a last musical sticker for your certificate. Cool!

Colour in your score.

Answers

Test 1 Number sequences
The missing numbers are:
1. 35 27 23
2. 47 65 74
3. 91 121 151
4. 22 29 36
5. 77 72 57
6. 109 105 101
7. 37 46 55
8. 195 185 165
9. 54 50 38
10. 120 115 110
11. 77 80 83
12. 91 88 79

Test 2 Addition and subtraction facts
1. 60
2. 1400
3. 500
4. 160
5. 80
6. 900
7. 60
8. 50
9. 1500
10. 50
11. 110
12. 600

Test 3 Shapes and symmetry
1. triangle
4. pentagon

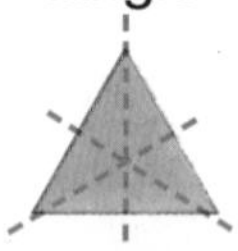

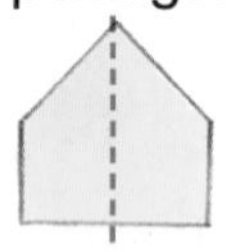

2. square
5. rhombus

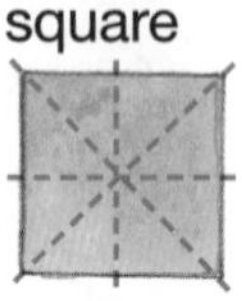

3. rectangle
6. hexagon

7
8
9

10
11
12

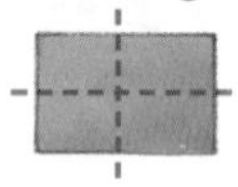

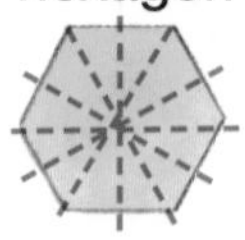

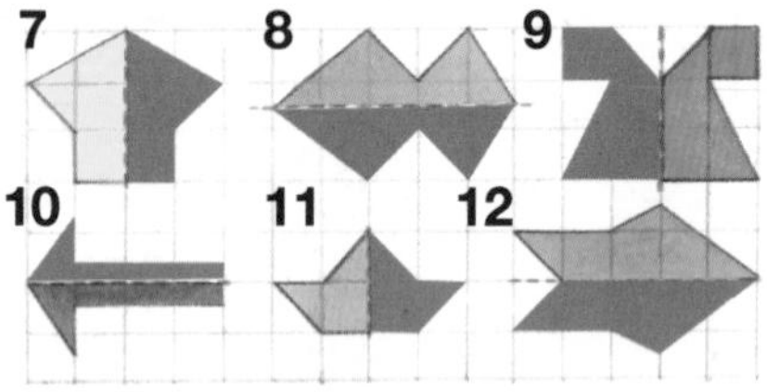

Test 4 4-digit numbers
1. 6000 + 700 + 10 + 2
2. 8000 + 900 + 90 + 3
3. 4000 + 100 + 50 + 6
4. 2000 + 300 + 50 + 6
5. 7000 + 500 + 90 + 8
6. 2000 + 100 + 10 + 5
7. 3000 + 900 + 60 + 5
8. 1000 + 200 + 50 + 4
9. 3000 + 400 + 80 + 9
10. 6000 + 900 + 30 + 2
11. 4000 + 300 + 70 + 5
12. 7000 + 900 + 90 + 7

Test 5 Comparing and ordering numbers
1. >
2. <
3. >
4. >
5. >
6. >
7. >
8. <
9. <
10. >
11. <
12. >

Test 6 Mental addition and subtraction
The missing numbers are:
1. 61
2. 64
3. 26
4. 35
5. 93
6. 33
7. 35
8. 29
9. 95
10. 29
11. 25
12. 101

Test 7 Area and perimeter
1. area = 24 squares
2. perimeter = 20 units
3. area = 6 squares
4. perimeter = 10 units
5. area = 5 squares
6. perimeter = 12 units
7. area = 9 squares
8. perimeter = 12 units
9. area = 20 squares
10. perimeter = 18 units
11. area = 25 squares
12. perimeter = 20 units

Test 8 Decimal numbers
1. 0.3
2. 0.5
3. 0.8
4. 0.9
5. 6.2
6. 6.5
7. 6.7
8. 6.8
9. 14.1
10. 14.3
11. 14.6
12. 14.9

Test 9 Equivalent fractions
1. $\frac{3}{6} = \frac{1}{2}$
2. $\frac{2}{8} = \frac{1}{4}$
3. $\frac{2}{10} = \frac{1}{5}$
4. $\frac{3}{9} = \frac{1}{3}$
5. $\frac{2}{12} = \frac{1}{6}$
6. $\frac{4}{8} = \frac{1}{2}$
7. $\frac{6}{8} = \frac{3}{4}$
8. $\frac{4}{6} = \frac{2}{3}$
9. $\frac{6}{10} = \frac{3}{5}$
10. $\frac{5}{10} = \frac{1}{2}$
11. $\frac{6}{9} = \frac{2}{3}$
12. $\frac{9}{12} = \frac{3}{4}$

Test 10 Multiplication and division facts
The missing numbers are:
1. 5
2. 63
3. 8
4. 40
5. 9
6. 8
7. 3
8. 8
9. 24
10. 9
11. 32
12. 9

Test 11 3-D shapes
1. sphere
2. cuboid
3. prism
4. cone
5. cylinder
6. pyramid
7. 6
8. 5
9. 5
10. 2
11. 3
12. 4

Test 12 Reading the time
1. 5.28
2. 11.13
3. 8.06
4. 4.41
5. 8.26
6. 7.46
7. 6.52
8. 11.11
9. 5.32
10. 2.51
11. 7.36
12. 4.59

Test 13 Written addition
1. 175
2. 192
3. 241
4. 264
5. 292
6. 243
7. 462
8. 497
9. 631
10. 424
11. 611
12. 772

Test 14 Multiplying and dividing by 10, 100 or 1000
1. 8900
2. 15 600
3. 39 500
4. 19 000
5. 78 000
6. 124 000
7. 340
8. 95
9. 367
10. 14
11. 36
12. 93

Test 15 Tables and graphs
1. Saturday
2. 19
3. Wednesday and Sunday
4. 13
5. Friday
6. 47
7. 45
8. Week 2
9. Week 2
10. 30
11. Week 2
12. 140

Test 16 Coordinates
  1 F   **3** B
  2 H   **4** I

  5 (7,2)   **7** (7,9)
  6 (0,4)   **8** (6,4)

  9 square
10 right-angled triangle
11 rhombus
12 rectangle

Test 17 Negative numbers
  1 −4   **2** −3   **3** −1   **4** 1
  5 −8   **6** −7   **7** −4   **8** −2
  9 −9 **10** −6
11 −4 **12** −3

Test 18 Fractions and decimals
  1 0.3   **4** 8.4
  2 0.6   **5** 19.8
  3 4.9   **6** 32.7

  7 $\frac{8}{10}$ or $\frac{4}{5}$ **10** $9\frac{1}{10}$

  8 $\frac{5}{10}$ or $\frac{1}{2}$ **11** $24\frac{6}{10}$ or $24\frac{3}{5}$

  9 $7\frac{3}{10}$ **12** $41\frac{2}{10}$ or $41\frac{1}{5}$

Tests 19 Fractions of quantities
  1 5   **7** 6
  2 15   **8** 24
  3 4   **9** 10
  4 8   **10** 30
  5 7   **11** 3
  6 21   **12** 15

Test 20 Multiples

Multiples of 3
21, 18, 24, 42, 27, 48, 66, 60, 72

Multiples of 4
40, 24, 32, 48, 60, 72, 64

Multiples of 6
18, 24, 42, 48, 66, 60, 72

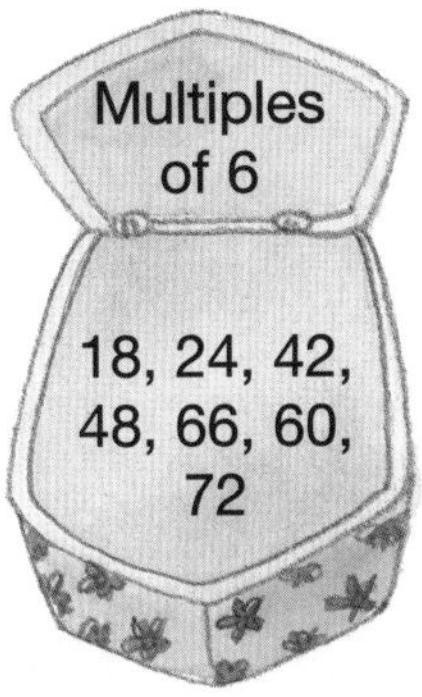

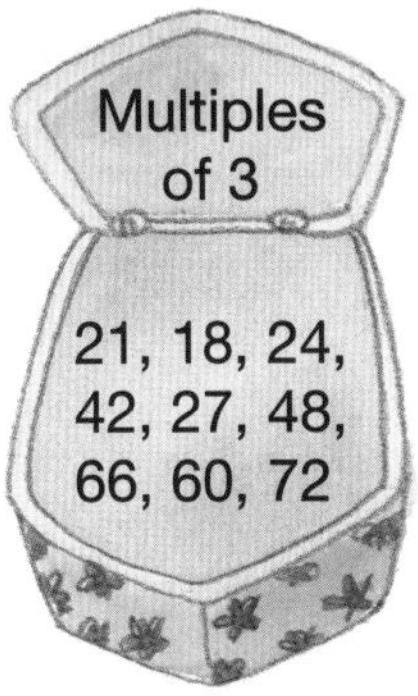

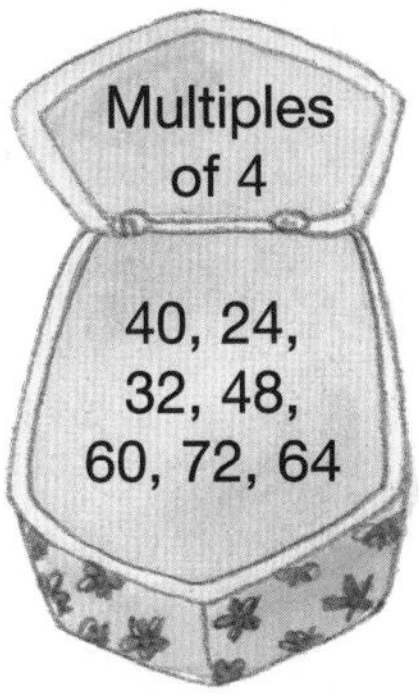

Test 21 Written subtraction
  1 108   **2** 117   **3** 118
  4 104   **5** 114   **6** 113
  7 59   **8** 57   **9** 79
10 89   **11** 78   **12** 84

Test 22 Rounding and approximate answers
  1 120   **7** 800
  2 160   **8** 1400
  3 220   **9** 1500
  4 80   **10** 900
  5 70   **11** 500
  6 70   **12** 900

Test 23 Written multiplication
  1 81   **2** 234   **3** 212
  4 335   **5** 492   **6** 455
  7 304   **8** 441   **9** 420
10 304   **11** 282   **12** 371

Test 24 Angles
  1 east
  2 east
  3 south
  4 east
  5 north
  6 north
  7 south
  8 south-east
  9 south-east
10 south-east
11 south-west
12 south-east

Test 25 Measures
  1 3kg   **7** 4250g
  2 $1\frac{1}{2}$m   **8** $3\frac{3}{4}$l
  3 4000ml   **9** 550cm
  4 2500m   **10** $2\frac{1}{4}$kg
  5 8cm   **11** 90mm
  6 $2\frac{3}{4}$m   **12** $6\frac{3}{4}$km

Test 26 Proportion
  1 $\frac{1}{2}$ **7** $\frac{3}{4}$
  2 $\frac{1}{4}$ **8** $\frac{2}{3}$
  3 $\frac{1}{3}$ **9** $\frac{1}{2}$
  4 $\frac{1}{5}$ **10** $\frac{3}{4}$
  5 $\frac{1}{4}$ **11** $\frac{3}{5}$
  6 $\frac{1}{5}$ **12** $\frac{1}{2}$

Test 27 Written division
  1 17   **7** 12
  2 26   **8** 14
  3 12   **9** 29
  4 14   **10** 19
  5 23   **11** 13
  6 18   **12** 24

Test 28 Reading scales
  1 120g
  2 150g
  3 170g
  4 190g
  5 4.3kg or $4\frac{3}{10}$kg
  6 4.9kg or $4\frac{9}{10}$kg
  7 5.5kg or $5\frac{1}{2}$kg
  8 5.7kg or $5\frac{7}{10}$kg
  9 4.5l or $4\frac{1}{2}$l
10 3.75l or $3\frac{3}{4}$l
11 2.25l or $2\frac{1}{4}$l
12 1.5l or $1\frac{1}{2}$l

Alien Club Certificate

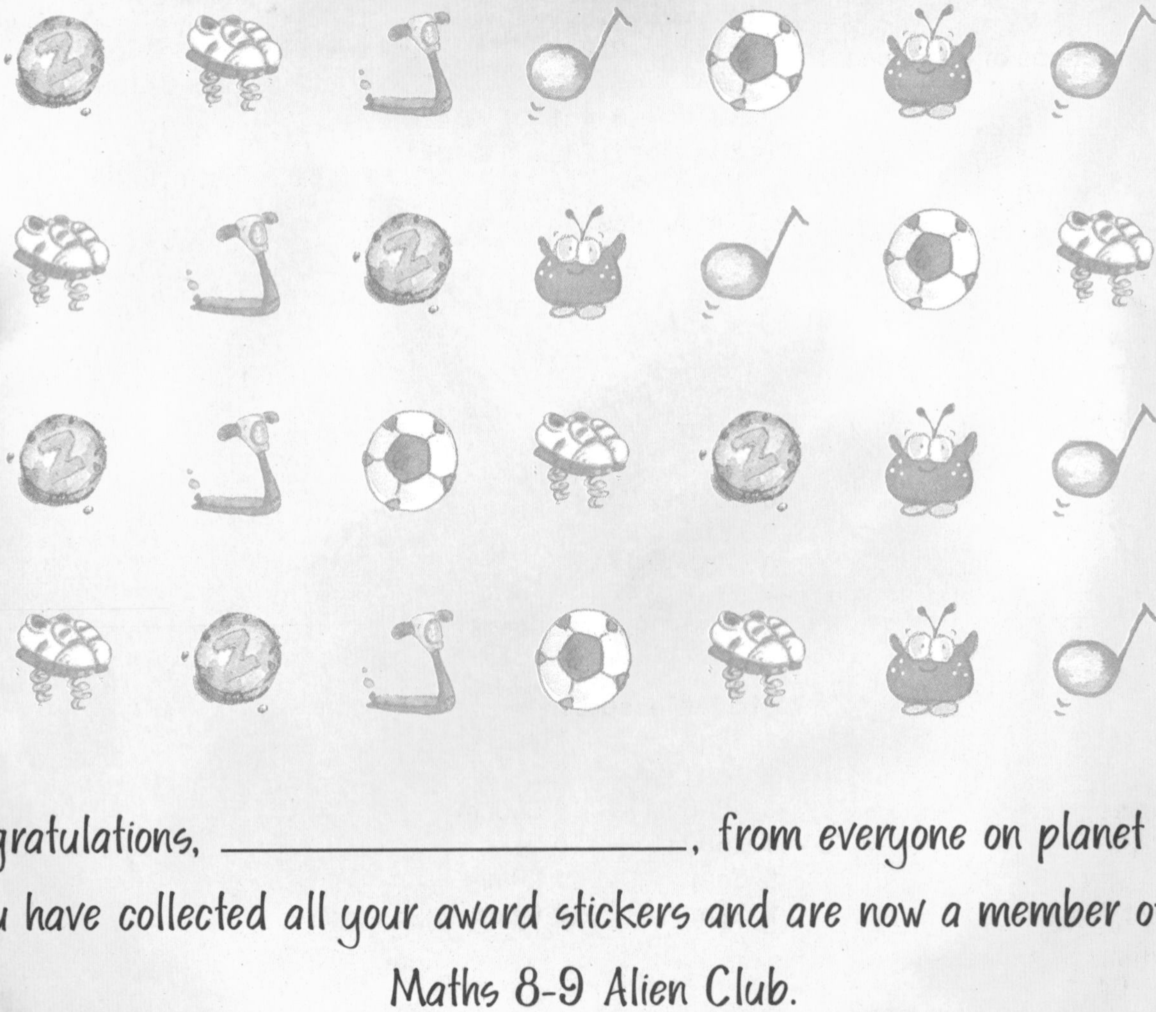

Congratulations, ______________________, from everyone on planet Dunk!
You have collected all your award stickers and are now a member of the Maths 8-9 Alien Club.

You are out of this world!

ZP